THEN PITY,
THEN EMBRACE

Then Pity,
Then Embrace

* * * * * * * *

BY NANCY W. BARTLETT

The Macmillan Company, New York
Collier-Macmillan Ltd., London

FIRST PRINTING

The Macmillan Company, New York
Collier-Macmillan Canada Ltd., Toronto, Ontario
Printed in the United States of America

For
Barbara Tuchman
and
Cecil Scott

CONTENTS

THEN PITY,
THEN EMBRACE

Prologue

IT WAS very early in the morning and it must have been springtime for the air smelled fresh and sweet. I was hurrying down the city street stretching ahead of me long and black and shiny—it had been raining. I was tired and the street kept unrolling before me as if there were no end to it. Would I never get there? I was worried—I didn't know why. At last I came to the house, our house, and was about to run in the side door, the door we always used, but —what was the matter? The door wasn't there! There was only a blank wall, and suddenly there were a great many people gathered around a man who was climbing a ladder with a paint bucket in his hand. They were laughing. I was ashamed. Were they laughing at me? I felt confused and very tired. I wanted so badly to get home. Then it came to me. Of course! I had forgotten! This wasn't our house any more. We had moved. This was the old house at 113 Sacramento Street where we had lived with Mother so long ago. There was the sign JAMES H. FLANNAGAN FUNERAL PARLOR. I hurried on.

At last I had to slow down to draw a breath. An old woman was walking swiftly, lightly toward me—so graceful it was as if she were dancing there on the city street. She stopped when she saw me and looked deep into my face.

"Are you all right?" she asked.

1

"Oh yes," I said. I was embarrassed but I told her. "It's funny but I can't seem to remember where I live."

She didn't answer but looked at me with a strange sad look. I was about to hurry on. I glanced at her again. It wasn't a woman! It was a man!—a very dark man with thick dark hair like a fur cap and heavy dark brows and black eyes. I felt frightened.

"Can I help you?" he asked.

"Oh no," I said. "Thank you, but . . ." and I found myself telling him, though I hadn't meant to, "the trouble is I can't seem to remember where I live."

"Why don't you come with me?" he said gently.

"No, no, I can't do that," I said loudly—almost shouting —and I began to run down the long street. He didn't try to follow, but I could hear him very close to me laughing softly.

The telephone was ringing sharply shattering my dream. I tried to sit up—"I arise from dreams of thee in the first sweet sleep of night"—but it wasn't night, was it? Or was it early morning? I glanced at the clock—four. It must be afternoon. I picked up the receiver and said hello.

"Amanda?" The voice was familiar, as familiar as the sound of my own voice or my sisters' voices or my daughters', but this was a man's voice, at once nasal and full bodied, a singer's voice. Of course, it was my former husband. "Is Liza there?" he asked briskly.

"No, she isn't," I said, "she's gone to the dentist's."

"Oh? When will she be back?" The tone was sharp, suspicious, as if I were telling a lie to keep him from talking to her.

"Pretty soon. Can I give her a message?"

"Yes, I'd like to see her and Stephen and the kids while they're here." The lift to the voice was cheerful, almost gay, so familiar—that gaiety. "Do you know if they're busy Christmas Eve?"

"Well—yes, they are. We're having a little gathering here Christmas Eve."

"I see." The lilt had gone. "Is Fee coming too?"

"Yes, she is," I said uncertainly. I wanted to plan some time when he could see them, but I didn't dare without consulting them; I had done it before and they hadn't liked it. "What about Christmas night?" I ventured. "I don't think they're doing anything then . . . " But I knew this wasn't what he wanted. In our family it was always Christmas Eve.

"I don't know." The voice was resentful now. "Well, ask Liza to call me." Now it was cold, impersonal.

"I will," I said.

I lay back on my bed and stared at the winter rain playing against my window. I felt troubled—uneasy. The dream and the call had upset me. Perhaps I could go back to sleep to black it all out. But my mind kept asking the same questions: Why had it happened this way? Could I have done it differently?

My gaze moved to the group of family photographs on the wall over my desk, to the one of Grandpa Evans with his astonishing side whiskers, protuberant lower lip and kindly gray eyes that seemed to be regarding me so solemnly. I thought of what he had once said about my father: "It took a thousand years to produce an Archibald Willard." He hadn't meant me to hear him; I had been listening as I usually did when he and Mother talked together. I had often puzzled over that remark when I was a child . . .

PART ONE

8 *Wellington Street*

MRS. RYAN'S HOUSE

MY LIFE opened on the afternoon of September 8, 1921, the day before my ninth birthday. My sister, Rachel and I were on our way from Winchester, New Hampshire, where we had spent three weeks with Miss Anna Speare in her cottage by Lake Forest. Before this afternoon a few episodes stand out clearly against a blurred backdrop, but from this date my memory runs in an orderly, chronological fashion pausing frequently, directed or no, to reproduce now scenes, now entire acts, surprisingly complete as to the details of sets, lighting, sound effects, musical accompaniment, and most of all, the appearance, gestures, costumes, and dialogue of the actors.

Mother had found out about Miss Speare and her cottage from an advertisement in the *Boston Evening Transcript:*

WANTED. Children to board summer by beautiful lake seven dollars week per write Anna Speare Winchester New Hampshire references furnished.

So Mother had written and in August she, my two sisters, and I had all gone up there on the train, and as soon as Mother saw that it was a suitable place she had returned to Cambridge taking Phoebe with her. It hadn't seemed quite fair that Phoebe wasn't to stay too but Mother had said seven was too little, that it was too much responsibility for Miss Speare. Besides Phoebe might get homesick. It was always that way with Phoebe because she was the baby.

We had had a pleasant time at Lake Forest but both Rachel and I were glad to be going home. Rachel, one year and three months older than I, was very responsible about traveling on trains. This one was hot and sooty; the more I wiped my hands on the red plush the blacker they got and Rachel made me go and wash them before we got to North Station, but even then we had another half hour.

I was bored and excited both at once. Small waves of pleasure kept running through me at the prospect of being home again with Mother and Phoebe and Bridget (our nurse girl who had lived with us since we were babies). I was particularly pleased with the present I was taking to Mother, a paper bag filled with damp moss, pebbles, and iris from Lake Forest; I could hardly wait to see her expression when she opened the bag. As each small wave receded I was left dull and dispirited, gazing indifferently through the dirty window at the joyless stretches now approaching, now flattening, now quickly vanishing. For some reason they reminded me that I was going back to school tomorrow. I didn't know whether to be glad or sorry.

September 9, the first day of school and my birthday, always began my year. Time then moved rapidly from the lower left-hand sector of an elliptically shaped circle in a counter clockwise direction through the thrilling holiday season toward Christmas, which stood at the lowest point of the curve, then dragged upward through the bleak months to lovely May, Phoebe's birth month and thence to June 20, the day school ended and Rachel's birthday. (It often struck me as exceedingly significant, but for what reason I wasn't sure, that she and I had been born on these two red-letter days.) After this it dropped quickly but dis-

appointingly—summer never living up to the promise of
May—to September again.

The conductor burst into the coach barking something
which meant we had arrived. As we got off the steps with
our big straw suitcase, our boxes, and paper bags filled
with presents for everyone, I saw Mother at the end of the
platform waving and smiling and walking quickly toward
us. She never ran because of her asthma. She was dressed
in her winter suit, the dark blue serge with the accordian
pleated skirt and the black frogs on the jacket, her winter
hat of black felt, which she always trimmed herself, with
dark red velvet roses and her black Groundgripper shoes,
the low ones. (She didn't put on her high shoes until November.)

Leaving Rachel to struggle with the heavy suitcase, I
raced forward and threw my arms around her neck so
vigorously that her hat, held on only by her hatpin, stood
straight up in back. She laughed gaily and settled it back
and kissed me. Then swooping down on Phoebe, who was
dancing with excitement, I hoisted her as high as I could to
show her and Mother how strong I had grown. To my
horror she gave a piercing shriek and burst into tears. In
dismay I looked at Mother.

"Poor Phoebe has frightful boils on her thigh—it hurts
even to touch her," Mother explained. (She never said
"bottom" or "behind"—they were vulgar—always "thigh"
or "buttock.")

Leaning over she soothed Phoebe, now howling steadily
and thoroughly enjoying herself. A fine greeting, I thought
bitterly.

"Now, girls, I must tell you all about our new house,"
said Mother as we drove along the Charles River in a
Checker taxicab. What a pleasure to ride in an automobile!
I loved it—so superior to that stuffy old train. (The insides
of trains were always disappointing after the dash and

clangor of their outsides.) "They moved us in the day before yesterday," Mother way saying, "and Bridget and I, and Phoebe, have everything nicely settled and ready for you. Rachel, you will share a nice little bedroom with Bridgie, and, Mandy, you and Phoebe have one all to yourselves. Oh, you're just going to *love* it! We're extremely fortunate to have such a nice place! You must all promise to be very ladylike and well behaved—of course I know you *will* be—because Mrs. Ryan doesn't usually take children—or dogs," she added chuckling (Mother had an odd chuckle halfway between a laugh and a cough which made you want to chuckle too), "but I told her my girls were very quiet and considerate," and she reached over and patted Rachel's hand and then, not to leave me out (Mother tried never to favor one over the other of us), smiled across at me as I sat opposite her on the jump seat.

The mild September breeze lifted my hair and again I felt a surge of joy at being home—and at something indefinable, the beauty of the afternoon perhaps, the river drowsing rosy and dimpled under the brilliant cloudless sky, the sycamore trees along Charles River Road dusty after the long summer, the weeping willows daintily trailing their laces along the edge of the softly lapping water. I rested my head on the fragrant leather of the front seat idly enjoying it all, wishing that we might go on this way forever, gliding effortlessly forward under the capable hands of the silent driver, so cozy all of us together—and carefree.

"... and you will go to a splendid school now," Mother was saying, her eyes glowing with pleasure; "Miss Baldwin, the principal, is a Negress, a perfectly wonderful person and a fine educator—I've talked with her—this is the reason I'm moving to this part of Cambridge—so you can go to the Agassiz School. It's one of the finest—if not *the* finest—public grammar school in Cambridge, or in greater

Boston for that matter. You see, girls, I *believe* in the public schools. *They* are the heart of our democratic system of government. As soon as I can get the other things in our lives settled, I'm going to get out and do some work for the public schools here . . . and there will be children there you will enjoy. Miss Baldwin says there are a number of Harvard professors' families living in the Agassiz School area. Oh you're going to like it so *much!* You just *wait!"*

Her enthusiasm was catching. As always, when Mother was in a happy frame of mind, I felt elated, lighter than air. Perhaps school would be fun after all.

Now we were crossing Harvard Square, still summer quiet before the opening of college, then along upper Massachusetts Avenue, where impressive mansions resplendent with captains walks, porte cocheres, and steep, winding driveways spread out on either side of us.

"That's my house!" Phoebe cried as we passed one particularly elaborate.

"There's mine!" I cried pointing at another.

Leaving this luxurious neighborhood, we turned off a few blocks before Porter Square and headed north in the direction of Somerville. Here were two family houses in rows and around the corner the tenement district. Just short of the city line we drew up at our new home, 8 Wellington Street, a dingy brown shingled two-family house.

I can feel again the joy that welled up from deep within me as we struggled with our luggage up the narrow front walk, smell again the fragrance from the small yard bursting with fall flowers, shrubs, a grape arbor, and a pear tree. The grapes were delicious, as we discovered that evening, but the pears were hard as stones and tasteless. Dozens of bees were buzzing round the flowers. Mrs. Ryan kept them for honey, we learned, and went out twice a week to collect it, swathed in yards of netting draped over a large hat, her hands protected by enormous gauntlets.

Mrs. Ryan was at the door to greet us, an old woman with a curiously wrinkled face, false teeth that moved when she talked, frizzled white hair—which we soon found was usually done up in curl papers with a pink ruffled dustcap over them, but this was a special occasion—and all smiles. She wasn't as pleasant when we got to know her better and could be really cross if we slammed the door or ran up the stairs too fast.

"What lovely little girls!" she said to Mother after we had been introduced. "You must be very proud of them, Mrs. Willard."

As we passed her front door on our way up to our flat, I caught sight of a very old man sitting at a table with a napkin arranged like a bib around his neck eating something from a bowl—apparently his supper though it was scarcely five o'clock! Mrs. Ryan didn't introduce us to him. I remember nothing more of old Mr. Ryan for Mrs. Ryan kept him tucked out of sight, except in the very early morning when he would shuffle out to Wellington Street with a broom and a dustpan and sweep up the horse droppings to fertilize his wife's garden.

The inside of our new house was not as pretty as the outside. The rooms were small and dark with flowered wallpaper and gilded gas jets on the walls, but the ugliness didn't bother Phoebe and me. We had a room all to ourselves. She raced down the dark hallway ahead of me and proudly threw open the door. I looked around me. The wallpaper was prettier than in the rest of the apartment, a pattern of blue flowers and pink birds and there was a wash bowl in the corner.

"Isn't it cunning?" Phoebe cried hugging me. "And Mandy, you can have the bed by the window." That was

generous of her. Both of us liked to wake up in the morning and look out of a window.

It was no novelty to us to be in a new place; we had
moved almost every year of our lives. First it was London,
then a large house in Brookline, then a small house in
Brookline, then after Father and Mother had separated, the
Westmore, an apartment house on Commonwealth Avenue, near the Fenway, which had a dining room downstairs
where we had our meals when Mother didn't feel like cooking. After that it was Marlboro Hall on the Charles River
in Cambridge across from the old Cambridge Boat Club.
We had gone to the public school there, but the children
were so tough Mother had to move again.

Each place had seemed a little worse than the last. In
Boston, of course, we could coast down the sidewalk into
Commonwealth Avenue when it snowed, or in good weather
ride our velocipedes on the Fenway, but some of our games
weren't as wholesome. Rachel and I, for instance, spent
hours in the back courtyard of the Westmore examining
neatly done-up packages containing discarded articles of
feminine hygiene until Mother found out. Across from Marlboro Hall in Cambridge we used to skate when the river
was frozen, until one day a boy was brought out gasping,
dripping, and vomiting quarts of water, and then Mother
forbade us that; and in nice weather we roller skated on the
sidewalks and played hopscotch, but none of this was like
having one's own yard to look at with flowers and bees and
a pear tree.

That night after we had gone to bed and Phoebe was
asleep, snoring gently (she too had a tendency to asthma)
in her little cot against the wall, I heard Bridget coming
softly up the stairs. It was her day off and she got home
pretty late now because she had a "fella" (Mother said we
must say "young man" or "beau," but Bridget called it
"fella" and I liked that better.) She and Mother were talk-

ing in the living room. When I heard the word "pebbles," I knew they were talking about my present to Mother from Lake Forest, and then I heard a trill of laughter from Mother—she and Bridget were always laughing about something—but it wasn't a mean laugh; she wasn't making fun of me. Mother never did that. Then I heard Bridget say something about "Timothy" which made Mother laugh again, so I knew they were discussing Bridget's fella.

Bridget McBreen had come to us when she was only thirteen, because she wasn't happy in the shoe factory in Brockton, and she had been living with us for five years now. She was much more a part of the family than Father. He hadn't lived with us very long and about all I remembered of him then was that he disciplined us like soldiers with curt commands—"March," "Up," "Out," "On the double"—probably because it was wartime, and not being in the army because of his family, he had no one else to give orders to.

When Bridget first came we were babies and Mother had needed someone to help her; after that she stayed on as a sort of companion to us and to Mother though we really couldn't afford her any more. Mother and Father had spent most of the money he'd inherited from his father when they were first married, and now that Father was struggling with his career in New York City he didn't send us much. Mother felt guilty about Bridgie, but she loved her so much she couldn't bear to let her go.

When Bridget first lived with us she wore middy blouses, serge skirts, and high laced boots and her hair in a long braid with a large black bow. But now she dressed in mannish-looking shirtwaists tucked into tight-fitting skirts and she did her hair up with large puffs at the sides, "cootie garages" she called them. (Mother said this was vulgar but not to say so or we'd hurt Bridget's feelings.) Now too she'd given up her high boots which Mother thought very foolish; one could catch cold so easily that way and it wasn't good for the metatarsal arches. Mother's father was a doctor.

Just as I was going off to sleep I heard Bridget tiptoeing down the hall to the bedroom she and Rachel shared. I hissed loudly, "Lala!" This was the name Bridget and I called each other, short for "lalapaloosa" which Bridget said meant pal. I had thought it a silly name at first but I'd got used to it.

"You still awake, honey?" Bridget whispered and she stole in and kissed me good night. I could smell the nice Lifebuoy Soap she always used—"good for B.O.," she said —and her cootie garages tickled my nose in a pleasant way.

"I'm awfully glad to be home, Lala" I yawned.

"And your mother and Lala are tickled pink to have you, honey. It's been awful lonesome with you and Rachie gone. We're going to have a merry whirl in this cozy bungalow all together. You can bet your bottom dollar on that!" and she tiptoed out again and softly shut the door.

THE SISTERS

Probably the reason Bridget made such a pet of me was because I wasn't as pretty as my sisters, being a rather forlorn child, thin and pale with teeth that protruded slightly; then too I'd been in an automobile accident when I was six years old, which had left me with a big scar on my left forehead and a smaller one on my cheek which spoiled my dimple, my best feature.

Rachel was beautiful, with dark curling hair and large dark eyes and "wild rose" coloring, as my Grandmother Willard called it. Rachel was my grandmother's favorite. Phoebe was chubby and dimpled, with gold curls, a turned-up nose, sherry-colored eyes, and a chiming laugh. She and Rachel had the bright coloring of the Willards, my father's side of the family; my looks came from Mother's side, more regular features, but ash-colored hair and green eyes. Mother insisted my eyes were gray and was forever boasting about "Amanda's solemn gray eyes just like her Grandfather Evans." She disliked green eyes because of Becky Sharp. I hated my looks, especially my hair, so thin it wouldn't curl nicely like my sisters; my Grandmother Willard, whenever I visited her, was always trying to make it curl but all she could manage was five curls, two on each side and one on top, and I always wished she wouldn't try but I didn't dare say so. We were afraid of Grandmother Willard.

Ever since my automobile accident Mother considered me "nervous" and treated me like a semi-invalid, which I disliked though it had its advantages. She was constantly trying to bolster up my confidence by insisting I was a remarkable actress, and she often told the story of my Great Aunt Hester, my grandmother's sister, who came to call one afternoon when we were very little, saw me hanging back from the others as usual and pointing at me announced: "Why, Eliza, this is the flower of the flock!"

None of this convinced me that I *was* the flower of the flock. Mother protested too much, but I thought it nice of Great Aunt Hester.

Whenever we took turns visiting Grandmother Willard in her big house in Wychmere, Maine, Rachel was always the one to stay the longest. (My grandmother could have us only one at a time because of her heart.) Phoebe and I didn't behave as well as Rachel and besides we wet the bed.

One of my earliest memories was of a summer morning just before my fifth birthday when I awoke and discovered that the pleasurable trip I had just taken to my grandmother's large luxurious bathroom was a dream and that the warm comfortable pool I was lying in was swiftly turning clammy. I was terrified. I was sure that under no circumstances would my grandmother believe I hadn't meant to do it. I was right. She punished me by tying a chamber pot around my waist over my rompers and making me wear it all morning. The cook and the handyman and the delivery people all saw me in this humiliating costume; I could hardly wait to get home to sob out my tale of woe to Mother who in turn was exceedingly angry and declared that I would not visit *there* again in a hurry. To tell the truth my grandmother did not invite me again for several years.

The day after our return from New Hampshire we started at our new school. The year before, when we lived near the Charles River, we had gone to the Lowell School where a number of unpleasant things had happened. I particularly remember one afternoon when Rachel and I were on our way home walking by the river, the upper reaches of which were a wilderness in those days, when a pack of rough boys came thundering down on us and the biggest of them jumped on Rachel while the others stood around yelling and jeering. I opened my good-sized mouth and screamed my loudest but there was no grown-up in sight. Seeing my beautiful sister forced to crouch under that horrible boy I knew a moment of pure terror. Then, perhaps because of my screams, the boy jumped off Rachel and they all ran away.

Now as we three set off for school in the refreshing morning hand in hand, with Phoebe in the middle, the familiar queasy sensation that always accompanied me on the first day of school began to reassert itself.

"Did you like second grade, Mandy?" quavered Phoebe, and realizing she was more uneasy than I, I suddenly felt not queasy at all but bravely confident.

"Oh yes, you'll love it," said I stoutly.

Rachel at Phoebe's other hand was far off, deep in her own thoughts; she lived in a world of her own, insulated from such humdrum matters as feeling nervous about a new school.

But Phoebe needn't have worried. Her teacher was young and pretty and Phoebe immediately became her pet just as she was everyone else's. The teacher's name was Dorothy Donnelly. I can readily remember the full names of all the teachers at Agassiz because they were without exception alliterative. There was Catherine Carr in the first, Hilda Hanlon in the third, Eileen Emery in the fourth (my own grade), Marietta MacDougall in the fifth (Rachel's grade), Letitia Lanahan, Dora Dodson, and Susie Simpson in the sixth, seventh, and eighth. Everyone at Agassiz called them by these names—behind their backs of course. None of them was young and pretty except Miss Donnelly; in fact they were old and some of them were cranky.

The children at Agassiz, though not as tough as those at Lowell School, came mostly from poor families—Irish Catholic, Italian, Greek, Armenian, and Negro. There were a few who came from backgrounds similar to ours, but they lived in a better neighborhood than Wellington Street and had more advantages than we did.

That first afternoon Rachel arrived home with two little girls whom Mother greeted cordially—she was always charming when we took any of our friends home to meet her—and after scrutinizing them carefully she exclaimed: "You must be Amelia Everett's daughters!"

The smaller one said no because their last name was "Whitman," but the bigger one said yes, their mother was Amelia Everett, one of Mother's most brilliant Radcliffe classmates. Rachel asked if she might go to their house to play and Mother immediately gave her consent. That evening Rachel returned glowing with enthusiasm, her former preoccupied manner evaporated.

"Oh, Mother, the Whitmans are so wonderful!" she said that night as we sat down, Mother, Bridget, Rachel, Phoebe, and I—Bridget always sat with us—to our supper of creamed chipped beef in our cozy new dining room. "And their house is wonderful! Big and comfortable with a playroom in the attic and a big yard!"

"Now you see why I wanted to move to this part of Cambridge, don't you?" said Mother her eyes shining, her voice triumphant. "Amelia Everett is a very unusual person. *They* are the kind of people I want my daughters to associate with!"

After that Rachel went almost every afternoon and on Saturdays to the Whitmans. But after the first afternoon she never brought the Whitman sisters to our house. I heard Mother ask her once why she never did and Rachel's reply: "Oh, Mother, it's such fun there—there's so much to do."

Phoebe too soon made friends at Agassiz, but some of her experiences weren't as satisfactory as Rachel's. To understand her situation properly I must explain that Wellington Street where we lived was a short street running between Museum and Wendell Streets. If you go there today you will still see a high wooden fence which runs the length of Museum Street dividing the poor section from the rich and fashionable Shady Hill section.

One of Phoebe's new friends, Judy Butler, lived in

Shady Hill just on the other side of this high wooden fence, and every afternoon Phoebe would crawl through a gap made by a missing board to find herself in another world of imposing houses and well-kept lawns. Even the trees were different, tall and green with luxurious leaves and of an infinite variety, in all shades of green and red.

Phoebe was very happy about Judy Butler; she loved to enter this fairyland world, but as the weeks went by she began to sense that things were not as they should be. One late afternoon she came home from Judy's house in tears. Mother was in town on some errands, Rachel was at the Whitmans, Bridget had stepped out to the grocery store for a few minutes, so she told her sad story to me. She and Judy had started up the stairs so that Judy could show Phoebe, who was longing to see it, her own little bedroom.

"She says it's so pretty, Mandy, with her own bureau and her own desk! Think of that! But just as we got to the top of the stairs Judy's mother yelled at Judy, 'You come down here this minute, Judy Butler. You know you're not allowed to take her up there,' and we had to go back to the sunroom—and, Mandy, she's so mean, she never lets us go anywhere but *there* for a minute—or outdoors in the laundry yard—and I know she lets Judy take Rosemary Taylor *every* place—and she never speaks to me at all, she never even says 'hello' to me when we come in, she just speaks *about* me. She says, 'Tell Phoebe to wipe her feet before she comes in the house,' 'Tell her—' she usually calls me 'her'—'it's time for her to go home,' 'Tell her you're going away tomorrow so not to come,' and today she said 'Tell her to wash her hands and face the next time she comes here'—and Mandy, my hands weren't even dirty, not the littlest bit, honest!" and here Phoebe sobbed so hard she couldn't continue.

"That settles it, Phoebe," Mother said grimly, when she

had returned from town and I had reported the situation to her; "you are *never* to set foot in that house again!"

"But I *like* Judy—she's my best friend," cried Phoebe, "It isn't her fault if her mother's mean."

"You may play with Judy at school, dearie," Mother was immediately gentle, "or you may ask her to come *here*, but I will not tolerate rudeness to my daughter. Mrs. Butler must not be—very well bred, I'm afraid."

So it was. Phoebe never went to the Butler's in Shady Hill again nor did Judy ever come to our house.

For some reason we almost never took our friends home. It was not that Mother was anything but charming and welcoming to them; when they met her they came away their eyes glowing with admiration.

One of the Whitman sisters said to me years later: "When I was a girl your mother was the most fascinating person I'd ever known. She was so pretty, so gay, the few times I ever saw her, so much fun to talk to . . . and there was something mysterious, romantic about her."

Yet none of them came more than once or twice. Perhaps Rachel was right. There was so much to do at other people's houses.

Although, like my sisters, I had no trouble making friends, in fact a whole band of loyal followers, with me there was never any question of playing at *anyone's* house. *We* played on the street. Sometimes when it rained we invaded the entryways of the various tenement or two-family houses—never of course Mrs. Ryan's entryway. That was understood.

Diagonally across the street from Mrs. Ryan's was an iron bar bordering the yard of the house on the corner where the neighborhood kids gathered after school. "Meet you at the bar" was the word. Here Rachel and Phoebe and I were introduced to our favorite game, kick-the-can, played like baseball with the street corners for bases. Since there were few cars in those days we could play uninterrupted for hours until Mother or Bridget rang the little silver bell that meant we were to go in. It was a great trial that we were never allowed to stay out as late as the others.

In poor weather when we stayed at home, we three sisters played a variety of odd games. There was the voyage to the moon, my invention, which consisted of standing with one foot on each doorknob, clinging to the top of the door and swinging back and forth, with me as moon man and buttons for admission. My sisters were usually obliging about letting me be the boss, a role I insisted upon, until Rachel would get bored and go into another room to read. Another game, scorned by Rachel but a favorite with Phoebe and me, was a voyage to the North Pole wrapped up in quilts, sliding down the back stairs (if Mrs. Ryan was out) or on Mother's big double bed which served as a sleigh with reins attached to the brass knobs at the foot.

Mother was nice about letting us play these games while she and Bridget talked and laughed together in the next room, Bridget ironing the clothes and Mother at her sewing machine. She was very fond of sewing.

GRANDPA EVANS

Soon after we moved to Mrs. Ryan's house Grandpa Evans came to pay us one of his lengthy calls. Phoebe and I had just come home from school, Rachel as usual had gone to the Whitmans to play, and we were breathlessly in the midst of telling Mother and Bridget all that had happened that day when we heard the front doorbell.

"Run down, girls, and let Grandpa in," said Mother and Phoebe and I sprinted downstairs. Next to Mother, "the old doctor," as he was called (his older son, my Uncle James, was the young doctor) was the most important member of our family. Before we reached it the front door was opened and we could hear him coughing and wheezing as he climbed the stairs. He had "the asthma" too. We flew into his arms.

"My little darlin's!" he said giving us each a large wet kiss straight on the mouth which, when his back was turned, we quickly wiped away. As always he had a five-pound box of Bailey's chocolates under his arm. We escorted him up the double flight of stairs and into the living room, where Mother kissed him affectionately and relieved him of his hat and coat.

According to Mother, Grandpa Evans had been a "stunning youth." She always said I looked just like him, which pleased me not at all for when I knew him he had a bald head, a large bulbous nose—which he was forever blowing vigorously until it was as red as Santa Claus—and white side whiskers that prickled when he kissed you. I used to feel a stab of guilt when I had to wipe away his kisses. He was such a good kind old man.

As soon as he was seated in his favorite chair and Mother in hers, a mahogany rocking chair she always sat in, one foot tucked under her, the box of chocolates was opened and passed around. Bridget took one, was urged to take several more, and then excused herself and went into the kitchen.

Phoebe and I were allowed to take as many chocolates as we liked. "Candy is good for them, Lizzie, just what they need for the blood," Grandpa said. Mother told us he said that because he liked it so much himself; he was not supposed to touch sweets because of his diabetes. Mother loved candy too and was always sending us to the corner store.

"Which one of you chickens will go to the store and get us each a candy bar? Get me an O. Henry and a Fat Emma and you get whatever you want. Here's twenty-five cents." I usually bought one large dill pickle for five cents and sucked it from its brown paper bag on the way home.

"And how are my little darlin's?" Grandpa asked us, drawing us to him, one on each knee and blowing his nose profusely with a large white hanky.

"Fine, Grandpa," we chorused.

"And do you like your new school?"

"Oh yes, Grandpa," and I was about to launch into a description of my new teacher but I could tell he wasn't listening, just smiling at us and saying "little darlin's, little darlin's" over and over until we got embarrassed and a little bored and finally retired to another part of the room.

Mother was coughing badly and breathing hard. She was having one of her spells that week, and Grandpa proceeded, as he always did, to give her a long lecture on what she ought to do. Phoebe and I had heard it so often we didn't pay much attention.

"Take the deep breaths, Lizzie, m'dear, take the deep breaths! That's what I always do and I'm a better man today than I was fifty years ago. I hope you're not a-smokin' that powder, Lizzie darlin', worst possible thing for the asthma, that stuff, breathin' that into your lungs. Take the deep breaths of fresh pure air, Lizzie, that's what you need."

When Mother's breathing was very difficult she inhaled something called "Jones Powder," which smoked when you lit it with a match; it came in a large flat tin with brown letters printed on it, and whenever she went out she put some into a small aspirin can in her handbag in case she got a bad spell from climbing subway stairs or when the cold air made her coughing worse. Stairs were the worst thing for Mother's asthma; she was always searching for escalators.

"Your Grandma Evans was a fine woman, children, a fine woman," Grandpa was saying to Phoebe and me. "None better, she came from fine old stock, fine old stock, but she *wouldn't* take the deep breaths, children, and that's why she died. You have to take the deep breaths, children," and he took several to show us, "if you want to be well and bein' well, my little darlin's, is next to being good —I know your dear mother has told you that. 'Cleanliness is next to godliness' the Bible says. That means good health, children. So always take the deep breaths."

Mother had gone out of the living room and we could hear her down the hall coughing terribly. I knew she wanted to smoke her Jones Powder but didn't dare for fear of an argument.

"And the dope, children," Grandpa continued, "the dope is the devil's own disciple. Never, never, *never* take the dope!" pounding the arm of his chair at each "never," his big voice resounding in the small room.

We had heard about the dope before. In fact we knew a great deal about it, for when Mother was having a really severe attack she had to take morphine prescribed for her by a doctor in Cambridge. It was no use her asking Grandpa to give it to her. He was dead set against it. The very word "morphine" set him off into tirades.

"Your Grandma Evans, children" he went on "was a fine woman, but she took too much of the dope, children. She . . ."

Mother came back in the room stifling her cough with a handkerchief held tightly to her mouth and leaning on the table for support, her knuckles white with the strain.

"Father, *please*," she said sternly between gasps, "don't

say *anything* more about Mother to the children. I can't
allow you to do that. My mother was a *wonderful* woman
and I don't want to hear a word—not a *word!*"

Grandpa looked hurt and I was afraid he might get up
and leave as he had once before when they had been on the
same subject; then Mother had felt sorry and had telephoned him, "Backbay 4425," to say she hadn't meant to
hurt his feelings. Fortunately just then Rachel came up the
back stairs and burst into the living room.

"Ah, here's my beautiful darlin'!" exclaimed Grandpa,
giving her one of his kisses. Glancing across the room at
her, at the dark red of her skin above the white collar of
her middy blouse, her glowing brown eyes, her shining hair
tumbled by the October wind, I thought how right he was
and a pang shot through me that I was so pale beside
her.

"Oh Mother," she cried after dutifully greeting
Grandpa, "the most *wonderful* thing! The Whitmans are
giving a party at Hallowe'en and they've asked me to come
—*me*—just think of it!"

A party was unusual. I felt a drop in my spirits that
Phoebe and I had not been invited but we were used to
Rachel's interesting adventures that didn't include us. If
Phoebe had been asked to a party and not me, that *would*
have been bad.

After we had talked about the party for a bit, Mother
asked Grandpa to sing to us. "Girls, I want you to listen
carefully now. Some day you'll look back and remember
that your grandfather at seventy-five had a voice like a
young man. It's true, Father, your voice is every bit as
clear and every bit as true."

"Nonsense, Lizzie, nonsense," said Grandpa but I could
tell he was pleased.

Grandpa almost always sang to us when he came to

call. His favorite songs were those he had heard Vesta Victoria sing: "There was I waiting at the church" and "John":

> *John took me down to see his mother,*
> *His mother, his mother,*
> *When he introduced us to each other*
> *She sized up everything that I had on,*
> *She put me through a cross examina-shun,*
> *I fairly boiled with indigna-shun,*
> *Then she shook her head, looked at me and said*
> *Poor John, Poor John.*

When he had gone Mother used to tell us how jolly he had been.

"It's hard for you girls to realize it, I suppose, at your age, but your grandfather used to be the gayest person you could possibly imagine. He was always laughing."

"Why isn't he gay now?" we would ask.

"Ah life is difficult," she would say sighing. "Life is difficult when you get old."

After the singing Grandpa repeated his lecture to Rachel about the deep breaths and the dope, while Phoebe and I went down the hall to our own room to play Slap Jack and then Rachel went in to her room to read. Rachel was always reading.

Mother and Grandpa sat on in the darkening living room talking in low voices. Phoebe was busy with the cards and paid no attention but I could hear some of what they said. They were talking about Father. I heard the word "Archie" and then: ". . . not a cent for five weeks now," in Mother's voice, then some low rumbling from Grandpa, then ". . . know for a fact he's been living with that woman spending every cent he earns . . . ," then Grandpa's voice much louder, another lecture I could tell: "Pray for them, Lizzie! Pray for those that despitefully use ya!"

After that there was the sound of Mother weeping, then her voice again, low and tremulous: ". . . don't think I can *do* it, Father. I used to think I could, but I don't have the strength any more—*or* the courage . . ."

"Never say that, Lizzie darlin', *never* say that. You have great courage. You *must* have great courage. You have three lovely children, Lizzie. They're worth more than *ten* of him put together. And take my word, Lizzie dear, you're *better* off without him, *better* off without him. . . . Now take this and don't say a word about it . . ."

"Thank you, Father dear. You're so generous and good to me. Thank you . . ." Her voice was very clear now. Phoebe had looked up from Slap Jack and was listening too. Grandpa was saying: "What else do I have to live for, Lizzie, in this world than my children and their little darlin's?" Then Mother called to us: "Girls, girls, Grandpa is leaving. Come and say goodbye."

So we all three went back to the living room where, before he left, Grandpa gave us each a five-dollar gold piece and another lecture.

"Love your enemies, children, that's what the Bible says," and I knew he was talking about Father and "that woman." "Love your enemies and pray for those that despitefully use ya! Pray for those that *despitefully* use ya!" with more thumpings on the arm of his chair and a fine spray of spittle at each "despitefully." He loved to quote from the Scriptures, not very accurately, as I found out in later years. "And remember, children, what the Bible says, never *touch* a drop of liquor or the tobacco and you'll live to be a hundred!" then more specifically to Rachel, who was only ten and a half but everyone thought of her as much older, "Beware of the devil and pray to God, my darlin', and ye'll be a fine woman like your mother."

Sometimes when Grandpa came he told us long stories about himself and his youth in Nova Scotia, to most of which I shut my ears. Various branches of his family had emigrated there from the Colonies at the time of the Revolution. Baptized Elijah Evans, he was "the seventh son of a seventh son" which meant good fortune, according to the farming people he grew up with, and it had turned out that way. He was the only one of his family to get an education. He came to Harvard College when he was fifteen, then on to Harvard Medical School, and after a long struggle, while he and his wife were very poor, he had made a striking success as a general practitioner. It was Mother's boast that her father had "the largest Irish Catholic practice in Boston."

His wife, also from Nova Scotia, came from a richer and more distinguished family than Grandpa's. I never knew her for she had died when Mother was still a very young girl, but according to members of her family she had great "tranquility of face and spirit."

Grandpa's stories were sprinkled throughout with his favorite admonitions about the liquor, the dope, the deep breaths, and the devil. Another popular subject was venereal diseases. Rachel and Phoebe and I knew all about gonorrhea and syphilis and how if people didn't behave themselves they could easily catch them.

"The wages of sin are death!" he would shout. Death in my mind was always connected with gonorrhea and syphilis.

Grandpa didn't mention death and disease today, nor did he tell us any tales of his youth. He had to get home to see an old patient. We went downstairs with him, all three, and he kissed us all again before he went off to the streetcar stop on Beacon Street in Somerville.

He usually came to see us by streetcar because my Uncle James needed the automobile to make his calls. Grandpa did not drive. He had a Negro chauffeur, Albert, whose wife, Bessie, was their housekeeper.

Occasionally Albert drove Grandpa to see us and on these days we'd be taken for a ride if the weather was fine, sometimes to Dover to the fine old farm where my Aunt Hildred, Mother's eldest sister, lived with her husband, Uncle Rupert, and their only child, little Rupert.

Sometimes we children went to the big brownstone front house on Westminster Avenue in what is now the South End in Boston, where Grandpa had his office in a large back room on the street floor and his waiting room in the spacious front drawing room awesomely furnished with massive pieces of mahogany upholstered in red plush. But Mother never accompanied us. Ever since the tragic death of her youngest sister, Belle, she had never set foot in her old home. We loved to play in the long drawing room, while Grandpa prescribed to his patients. Mother told us how, as a little girl, she and her brothers and sisters had often found quantities of silver pieces in the depths of the enormous couch, where presumably they had slipped from the pockets of the waiting patients. It was a favorite occupation plunging our hands deep down behind the cushions for loot that was never there.

Grandpa always introduced us to his patients as they went out: "You remember my daughter, Eliza? These are her darlin' little girls."

After they had departed he would hand out interesting bits of information: "You see that young lady, children? Her mother used to scrub floors—and now she's a fine woman—married to one of the richest men in Boston," or "His son, a beautiful boy, is dying from the liquor. Stay away from the liquor, children! Stay *away* from the liquor and the tobacco if you want to have a good life!"

When Grandpa Evans grew old and feeble and could no longer go downstairs to see his patients, those who had been coming to him for years went upstairs to his bedroom. "He kept up his practice until the day he died" his family always said. If one of us children happened to be there when he was confined to his bed, we would go up and read the newspaper to him because his eyesight was failing so badly. He would listen for only a few minutes, then plunge into a long anecdote about some member of the family, often about himself and his brothers in Nova Scotia, "the black devils," as they were called because of their mischief and their dark skin (there was a Spanish ancestor somewhere in the background), or he would talk about his wife's family:

"Fine old stock, Amanda, never forget that, they're fine old stock!"

One episode at Westminster Avenue that made a deep impression on me occurred when Grandpa was very old. It was early in the evening in winter time. Bessie, the housekeeper, and I were downstairs in the kitchen having a cup of tea when the doorbell rang; I ran up to answer it to find a Negro standing outside, hatless and coatless in the bitter weather, his white eyeballs rolling.

"Is the doctor in?" he asked hoarsely.

"Yes," I began when Bessie came rushing to the door.

"The doctor's too sick to see anyone," she said tersely.

"But my wife's dying!" the man begged, his face almost white with anxiety.

"I'm sorry," Bessie said firmly shutting the door in his face.

I was shocked and dashed upstairs to tell Grandpa who I knew was not that ill, for I'd just been listening a half hour before to a long tale of his youth with as vigorous thumpings as ever, but he only shook his head.

"It's all right, darlin', it's all right," he said.

It wasn't all right with me, however. For days afterward I was inconsolable at my grandfather's heartlessness. When I went home that night Mother tried to explain that he had this kind of call many times a week and could not possibly answer them all, that undoubtedly the man would have found another doctor who could attend his wife, but none of this satisfied me. I could only find it possible to forgive my grandfather because it was the one unkind thing he ever did as long as I knew him.

Years later my father liked to tell a story about Grandpa, of whom he was exceedingly fond. "The old doctor," as Father called him, had visited them in Brookline, after my Aunt Belle's death, before Father and Mother were separated. As usual he was constantly railing against the dope, the devil, the tobacco, and the liquor. After he had gone they found hidden away in a dark recess of the guest room closet a whole box of empty whiskey bottles. Father always laughed uproariously when he told this story, but I never thought it was at all funny.

FRAGMENTS

During that fall and winter at Mrs. Ryan's house, Mother began to emerge for me, fragment by fragment, as an individual personality, separate and distinguished from her heretofore simple role as mother to Rachel and Phoebe and myself.

It was on a rainy October afternoon that she had the peculiar telephone mix-up. Mrs. Howard, a friend, whom Mother saw occasionally but usually visited with by telephone, was one of the few people she had kept in touch with since her separation from Father. The Howards had been kind to us, twice inviting us to their house in Nahant and, although Mother hadn't much use for Mr. Howard— "a weak fish and he drinks"—she was fond of Mrs. Howard. Bridget had gone out that afternoon and we three girls were off to the moon or the North Pole when Mother suddenly burst in on us, her eyes glittering: "Girls, girls, come quickly! You won't believe it!"

She pulled us in to the living room and, with her finger on her lips, picked up the receiver to the telephone and held it out to us. She had tried a few moments before to telephone Mrs. Howard, the wires had crossed, and she had accidentally been let in on a conversation between Mrs. Howard and another woman. They were discussing Mother! We three stood horrified. Mrs. Howard's loud nasal voice could be heard reverberating from the instrument: "I'm a trained nurse, you know, and I promise you I can spot a really sick person when I see one and Eliza Willard is no more sick than I am!"

Something from the other woman, then:

"That's right. It's all in her *mind.* Every bit of it. Why, the other day she told me she was down and out with asthma and the next thing I knew she'd gone in town!" A loud disagreeable laugh, then: "I don't blame the poor fellow for leaving her." Another horrid cackle.

"Mother, hang up, *please,*" Rachel whispered urgently but Mother held up her hand for silence. So we stood we four, while the conversation continued, Mother so still it was as if she were hypnotized, her short upper lip drawn back, a strange expression in her narrowed eyes, a mixture it seemed to me, of triumph at her friend's treachery—"I always knew that woman was false"—and pain.

We never saw any of the Howards again.

In her dealings with us Mother was seldom anything but sweet tempered; she never once spanked us, indeed scarcely reprimanded us for the usual childish transgressions. Father's side of the family said she spoiled us. Great Aunt Hester in later years told how one afternoon, when she came to call, we were all three on roller skates in the living room, jumping from the top of the piano to the keyboard to the floor, while Mother sat calmly in the next room reading a book. I don't remember anything of the kind, but certainly she was unusually patient with our misdemeanors, sometimes almost unaware, it seemed to me, that we were in the same room with her, except on occasions when we offended in the slightest degree her strict moral code.

One morning during that fall when Mother happened to come in on Phoebe and me in bed together having a fit of the giggles over some bit of nonsense she became so angry we were frightened. Her eyes narrowed, the nostrils of her fine high bridged nose quivered, her upper lip retracted tightly against her teeth.

"Girls, get *out* of that bed this *instant!*" she stormed, her voice shaking with fury, each word clearly enunciated, each *s* sibilant, "and don't ever again, either one of you, behave in that fashion as long as you live!"

Dumfounded as we were, we knew better than to argue. It was not until I was a grown woman that I realized the reason for this outburst: she must have assumed that we were indulging in some form of childish sex; such behavior could lead only "straight down the path to destruction."

Public figures were often the recipients of her strongest feelings. Woodrow Wilson, according to Mother, was "carrying on" with his second wife before his first wife "is in her grave"; Calvin Coolidge she thoroughly admired, laughing heartily at his laconic wit; Warren Harding she despised—"a weak fish and unprincipled"; David Lloyd George was a "splendid orator."

Like many people of her generation she knew the British royal family almost as well as her own: "tragic" Queen

Alexandra whose throat was "enameled" to restore the beauty ravaged by syphilis contracted from her husband, King Edward, that "miserable man, weak and dissipated and rotten to the core!" Queen Victoria she revered above all others.

But my mother's nature had another side: a passionate enjoyment of things and a great spirit of fun and gaiety. Even in the midst of a tirade something would strike her as funny and, from a flow of stern injunctions and solemn forebodings, she would break into peals of laughter, or she would decide that she had been sad long enough and that she must "perk up."

On that same morning when she had been so severe with Phoebe and me, she came into our room a few minutes later to say beamingly:

"Girls, I have the most *wonderful* idea! Harry Lauder is in town at the Boston Opera House. He is one of the greatest, if not *the* greatest actor and singer in our generation—and oh he's so funny! Just think, he was the son of a poor Scottish miner. How would you like me to get tickets—for this evening if I can? Don't you think it would be great *fun* for all of us to go?"

One of our diversions in those days at Wellington Street was to sit with Mother around the piano while she taught us her favorite songs:

". . . Now listen, listen to the voice of the piano—and listen to your own voices. Lovely, Phoebe, lovely! Listen to that child sing! You don't hear many seven-year-olds carry a harmony like that! You're going to have your Grandfather's voice—*and* your father's—he had a sweet clear voice too."

But the greatest fun in those early days was the dancing. Never athletic as a girl, Mother had been considered the most accomplished and graceful dancer in her group. "Eliza could make anyone who danced with her look like an expert," her sister Hildred used to say proudly.

Many was the afternoon or early evening at Wellington Street, when, seated at our upright piano in the living room, Mother would play waltzes or polkas for us, calling out directions as she played, jumping up every now and then to whirl us around the room.

"Make a hoop, Mandy! Make a hoop with your arms! That's right. . . . Good, Phoebe, good for you! That's it! That's it! Look at her! She's got it! Now with me—one, two, three, Rachel, you and Mandy together. Here we go! One, two, three!"

In our younger days she had taught us the Oxford Minuet. "Now point your toes, pause and *smile*, smile at your partner—this was a very *romantic* dance, remember— Right! Right!"

As tiny children of three or four years old she had started us off with a simple little dance, singing as she stepped it out for us:

> *How do do my partner, how do do today-ay*
> *Will you dance in a circle?*
> *I will show you the way—*
> *Tra la la la la la, Tra la la la la la*
> *Will you dance in a circle?*
> *I will show you the way.*

It never occurred to me that my mother was at all beautiful or even pretty. Her nose was too large to suit my idea of feminine beauty. I favored the doll-like Colleen Moore look.

It pained me too that she appeared so old and dowdy when I wanted her gaily and prettily dressed and above all youthful looking. She wore her skirts, as she always had, sweepingly full and almost to the ankle, although skirts were now tightly fitted and climbing higher each year.

She considered the dark blue serge suit with the black frogs and the accordian pleated skirt, which she had had

made in her youth at Hollander's, "very handsome."
"Good taste is always in style," she used to say, and she
wore it year after year for her excursions to Boston, the
only excursion she took when I knew her, although we
all three entreated her to buy herself something new; and
she trimmed and retrimmed her two black hats, one of felt
and one of straw, with feathers, roses, and pompoms, de-
pending on the season. Her high laced boots and dark lisle
stockings were not at all fashionable. The flesh colored silk
stockings now in vogue Mother thought disgusting—
"banana legs" she called them. She never "touched" make-
up of any kind; powder and rouge were "vulgar" and no one
except actresses wore lipstick.

Great Aunt Hester used to say "Eliza Evans had a high
bred look." Certainly everything about her was delicate,
finely drawn. Her figure was slight with tiny hands and feet
and slim ankles. Her hair, a cloudy gray mist about her
small head, very pretty as I think back on it, she wore in
the Gibson Girl style of her youth, puffed out at the sides
with a pug on top. Like mine it was thin and fine; on the
days when she went out she curled it with a curling iron
to give it more substance before doing it up.

"Your mother used to be *so* particular about her person,
especially her hair," Aunt Hildred told me once, "and she
always had the prettiest clothes when she was a girl!"

Sometimes in the evenings at Wellington Street Mother
let Phoebe or me take a brush and make curls the way
Grandmother Willard did with us. I can see her now sitting
patiently before the mirror laughing at her reflection, while
we fussed away at her, the long gray sausages hanging
down her soft cheeks, a blue bow perched on the top of her
head.

"I look like a very old and very tired doll," she would
say chuckling.

"No, you *don't*," we would protest, "you look much
prettier that way."

Her large delicate aquiline nose, surprising in her small face, gave her an aristocratic air. "I inherited my nose from my mother," she would say, carefully placing her thumb and middle finger along its fine bridge. Her teeth were very white, "blue white" was her boast, in contrast to Grandmother Willard's and Father's which, according to her, were "yellow white—but handsome and strong—much stronger than mine." Her gray-blue eyes were keen, the expression of her face sensitive with a sweet rather sad smile.

She was inordinately shy of having her picture taken, probably because no photograph ever did her justice. The only one I have of her, a blurred enlargement of her head in profile, taken from a small full-length picture of her with Rachel at three months, shows her with her wreath of soft hair, her prominent nose, and her sweet sad smile looking down at her baby.

One afternoon that fall at Wellington Street, Rachel and Phoebe and I went in town with mother on one of our excursions. On Bridget's afternoons out Mother loved to take us in town shopping; although she never bought herself clothes it was her pleasure, when she could afford it, to buy something pretty for us. We were sitting in the streetcar, Mother between Rachel and Phoebe, with myself opposite, when to my surprise the woman beside me turned and asked: "Is that your mother?"

"Yes," I said shyly, wondering what was coming next.

"She has a lovely face, hasn't she?"

I looked over at Mother, as she sat with one hand restraining Phoebe, who was on her knees looking out the window, the other hand smoothing a stray lock of Rachel's hair. She smiled fondly over at me. She *does* have a lovely face! I was astonished. It was the only time while she was alive that I ever thought of her in that way.

THANKSGIVING

A few weeks after Grandpa Evans' visit, when Mother had finally rallied from her latest bout of asthma, Phoebe and I arrived home from school to find her gone to town and Bridget in the kitchen, ironing the clothes, her hair in a pigtail down her back. She wore her cootie garages only when she "stepped out."

"Hi, girlies!" she called gaily. "How did it go today? Okey dokey?"

"Where's Mother?" Phoebe asked fretfully. She was never quite happy unless Mother was there.

"She's had to go in town—poor sweetheart—to confab with those lawyers—you know—for the trial."

Yes, we knew. Mother talked of nothing else these days, every single tiny detail she talked about to Bridget and to us. Next to her separation from Father, the automobile accident was the most important event in her life. By the time we had moved to Wellington Street all of us except Mother were bored with the accident and everything to do with it.

"Hey, Bridgie," I said, "you promised the next time Mother was out to finish teaching us that song. Remember?"

"What song, Lala? Oh sure, the one about the canoe. All rightie, I'll do that little thing as soon as I polish off this ironing. You girlies run and get my uke." Needing no second urging, Phoebe and I rushed to the room Bridget shared with Rachel to the neat little corner where Bridget kept her things. She knew all the latest songs and on days when Mother went in town she taught them to Phoebe and me. Soon we were all three tucked up on Bridget's bed singing to the ukelele:

I was all alone in my little canoe
And there was lots of moonlight all around,
I picked up a girlie in my little canoe
And we paddled all around the sound,
I told her she must kiss me or else get out and swim,
I heard a splash and she was halfway in and
I was all alone in my little canoe
And there was lots of moonlight all around.

Phoebe and I considered this song the height of wit but we were sure that Mother would not approve; she had an intense dislike for "improper" songs. Since it seemed wiser not to risk putting her to the test we did our singing on her in-town days. She had absolutely forbidden us or Bridget, for instance, to sing "When the red red robin comes bob bob bobbin' along," though none of us could understand why. It seemed such an innocent song.

Although only seven, Phoebe had already learned to play some chords on Bridget's ukelele; I had tried my best to learn and Bridget had done her best to teach me but it was no use. My forte was knowing all the words of every verse and, once I had learned it, I could carry the melody with no trouble.

In the midst of all this the telephone rang; Bridget had to put down her uke and go answer it. In a minute she returned with the news that, since Mother was in town and Rachel at the Whitman's, Bessie, Grandpa Evans' housekeeper, wished to speak to me.

Bessie's husband, Albert Snow, who was considerably older than she, had been with Grandpa Evans for many years, ever since the time when my mother and her brothers and sisters were very young. In those days Albert had been Grandpa's coachman; Mother liked to describe how stunning he had looked in his dark coat, high up on his perch at the front of their barouche, his handsome black face a perfect accompaniment to the span of gleaming black ponies.

It was not until a number of years after Mother and Aunt Hildred and their younger brother, Frederick, had been married and moved away from Westminster Avenue, when horses had been replaced by automobiles, that Bessie, a pretty young Negress, came to the house as second maid. At that time my Aunt Belle, still unmarried, was living at home and keeping house for Grandpa and for Uncle James, Mother's older brother, who was still a bachelor. Bessie had stayed with the family all through the terrible time of Aunt Belle's death, had married Albert soon after, and for a number of years now had been housekeeper.

She and Albert were like members of the family; the family always said Grandpa treated them more like his children than his servants. Albert, grizzled now, his face no longer gleaming black, still drove for Grandpa, but his chief job was that of general caretaker, valet, and bodyguard. Everyone loved Albert and Bessie was a particular favorite with us children.

"Hello, Amanda, dear" she said. "How are you all?"

"Oh, very well, thank you, Bessie, and how are you and Albert and Grandpa?"

"Just fine, honey."

"Mother's gone in town to see some lawyers about the trial."

"Yes, I know, so I thought I'd like to talk to you, Amanda. You can give Mother the message. Your grandpa would like to have you all come to Thanksgiving dinner. We're going to have a lovely big turkey and plum pudding and Albert is going to help me do everything so your mother can have a nice restful time. Aunt Hildred and Uncle Rupert will be here and little Rupert. Grandpa's very anxious to have all his grandchildren together. Uncle James won't be here though. He has to go to Chicago to a medical convention. It's too bad he has to miss Thanksgiving."

"Yes," said I halfheartedly. I could muster up very little disappointment that Uncle James was not to be there. We children hardly knew him; he never came to see us and whenever we went to Westminster Avenue he was out making calls, at the hospital, or busy with his patients. He never emerged from the back office, as Grandpa did, to greet us or to introduce us to his old patients. On the few occasions when we did see him he never said more than a barely polite hello or goodbye. It was hard to believe that he had been, as Mother told us, "a dashing young man."

"You'll urge Mother to come, won't you Mandy?" Bessie was saying.

"Oh yes," said I eagerly savoring already the turkey and cranberry sauce and plum pudding.

". . . and don't forget to tell her Uncle James will be in Chicago . . ."

When mother came home in the late afternoon dressed in her long black sealskin coat, for the weather had turned bitter, her blue eyes sparkled, her soft cheek cold as we kissed it, and I had hopefully delivered the message from Bessie, she bit her lip and turned away.

"I don't know, girls, I don't know. I'll have to think about it. I'm afraid we may not be able to do it this year."

"But we *never* do, Mother," Rachel cried, "and I'd *love* to go."

"Why can't we?" I demanded crossly and Phoebe began to cry.

"Now, girls, listen for a moment," said Mother taking

off her coat and the black hat with the pompoms and drawing us to her rocking chair, the seat of all our family conferences, "There's a perfectly wonderful moving picture coming to Boston. *Peter Pan!* It opens on Thanksgiving Day. I saw Maude Adams do it on the stage. I've never known such excitement in a theater. She *was* Peter Pan. When she stepped forward to the footlights and asked the children to clap for Tinker Bell the whole audience, children and grown-ups, broke into such applause I thought the house would fall! But they say *this* girl is very good. Betty Bronson. Sir James Barrie picked her himself . . ."

"But I'd rather go to Grandpa's," I broke in.

"Amanda," said Mother sternly, "Grandpa hasn't been well this fall and too much company will be very tiring for him at this time. He's not as young as he used to be, you know."

"But Bessie said he *wanted* all his grandchildren together. That's why they're having it—on *account* of Grandpa," I interrupted impatiently.

"Amanda, you don't know these things as well as I do. Bessie isn't always as considerate of Grandpa as she should be and she shouldn't have delivered the invitation to you. She knows that."

"I like Bessie," I said, "and she said it would be a nice rest for you, you wouldn't have to do anything, Uncle James won't be there, so there won't be so many people . . ."

"He will *not* be there?" There was a sharpness to her voice whenever she spoke of her older brother.

"No," I said. "Bessie says he's going to Chicago. So *can* we go?" I added eagerly.

Mother's answer was a deep sigh.

"Why are you mad at Uncle James?" Phoebe asked.

"Phoebe, dear, you must not say 'mad at.' It's poor English. Say 'cross with,' and" she continued patiently, "I am not cross with your Uncle James."

"But you don't seem to *like* him," insisted Phoebe.

"No, dear, you are mistaken. It's not that I don't like him. James and I used to be very fond of each other when we were young, very fond. Whenever we went to parties I was always his first partner. He used to say he'd rather waltz with his sister, Liza, than any girl in Boston—and James was a very popular young man . . ."

"What happened, Mother?" said Rachel.

"Well—Uncle James had a very unhappy love affair. That's why he never married. And he changed from a gay, carefree youth into a bitter man—so bitter I can't believe it's my brother James who . . ." She stopped speaking and put her head in her hand.

"But, Mother, is that why you don't like to go to Grandpa's house?" Rachel asked gently. "I thought it was because of Aunt Belle's death."

"Yes, yes." It was Mother's turn to be impatient. "And you know about that, all of you, so let's not talk any more about it."

It was true. We had been told more than once about Aunt Belle's death, so sudden and when she was still a very young woman, how she had been perfectly all right the day before, and then how they had found her, dead in her bed from a heart attack. Mother had been so upset at her death, she had loved Aunt Belle so much, she couldn't bear ever again to go to her old home. We didn't ask her any more questions because it always distressed her when she talked about her dead sister.

So we went into Boston on Thanksgiving Day to see Betty Bronson in *Peter Pan*.

A VISIT FROM FATHER

Early in December we received a telegram from Father saying he was to be in Boston on business and would come to call that afternoon. Father always did things abruptly.

My father, Archibald Paine Willard, Jr., at this time still a young man (he was eight years younger than my mother according to his side of the family, six according to hers) had had an unconventional background. His father whose family were nineteenth-century barons of Millwood, Massachusetts, where they had amassed a fortune in the paper business, had retired from the family business soon after his marriage to Grandmother Willard and had gone to Rome to live, taking his young wife and two small sons. Grandmother Willard had hated living so far from her own family, mostly ministers and teachers from Massachusetts and Maine, and after her husband's death from typhoid at the age of thirty-eight, had returned and settled down in their big summer house in Wychmere, Maine, which was to be Father's home until his marriage to my mother.

I had not seen my father since the time of my automobile accident and then only for a few moments when he had come to call on me in my hospital room, where my face had been so covered with bandages that I could hardly get a glimpse of him or the enormous chocolate Easter egg he had brought me.

My early memories of my father are fragments: riding to the beach in his Stanley Steamer, hearing his boyish musical laugh as he stood in the shallow surf while Rachel and I sputtered and struggled with our water wings, listening to him sing, along with Caruso on the phonograph, in his husky tenor voice, snatches from *Rigoletto* or *Pagliacci*.

The only episode that stands out in my memory as anything but a fragment is not a happy one.

We were living then in Brookline before Father and Mother were separated, so I must have been about four years old. It was late at night and I was awakened by the sound of my mother's voice calling out, "No! No!" and then a loud noise as of something falling.

Terrified I jumped out of bed and started down the dark hall toward my parents' bedroom. I clearly remember creeping down that hall and standing at their bedroom door uncertain what to do. The door was not entirely closed. Everything was quiet now and I was about to turn and creep back to bed when I heard Mother speak.

"I can't *stand* it any more, Archie! I just can't stand it!"

"And I can't stand your bloody jealousy!" Father's voice was very rough.

I waited a moment and then very softly I pushed open the door. In the half darkness I could make out their figures: my father naked except for a towel round his hips, his back broad shouldered and narrow hipped, a chair tipped over at his side, my mother in her high-necked white cotton nightdress sitting on the side of the bed, her head in her hands weeping. I was about to rush to her side to comfort her when she suddenly raised her head and said fiercely: "You're a *wicked* man, Archibald Willard, a wicked, wicked man!"

I must have gasped at this because my father wheeled around, saw me standing there and striding to the door shouted at me: "*You* go back to bed this *minute*, you damn little brat!"

While I stood there frozen, unable to move, he raised his

arm as if to strike me, but at this, Mother, who had got to her feet, without moving a step toward us or raising her voice, spoke and her words came like the lash of a whip: "Don't you *dare* strike that child!"

Father dropped his arm and brushing past me made his way through the door and down the hall to the bathroom. Mother soothed me and put me back to bed.

That is all I remember. Like a dream the episode was far at the back of my consciousness. It was only at times like this when Father came to see us that it returned out of deep layers of memory.

That morning in December being a Saturday, all of us except Bridget, who was with her family on vacation, were at home and set to work immediately preparing for his visit. It puzzled me that Mother should spend so much time cleaning and airing every corner of our flat when she seldom had a kind word to say about him.

Always exceedingly punctual, he arrived on the dot of three, just as his telegram had said. We spotted him through the window as he strode down Wellington Street looking quite out of place there, very dashing in his beautifully tailored chesterfield, with his derby hat and walking stick and, something new to us, he was sporting a mustache.

Phoebe dashed downstairs and threw herself into his arms. We could hear his ringing laugh as he came up carrying her on his shoulder. At a nod from Mother, Rachel moved forward to greet him and he put his arms around her and kissed her tenderly. Phoebe was a pet with him as with everyone else. He chuckled at everything she said, but Rachel was his special child. I hung back shyly longing to greet him as the others had but a little fearful—and resentful too.

I had forgotten how handsome he was, long and lean with thick dark hair, large dark eyes, and a way when he laughed of looking at you, his eyes wide open, his dimples flashing, as if to say: "Now, isn't *that* the most delightful thing you ever heard!"

But Mother was the one who amazed me. What a transformation! She was wearing her blouse of heavy white "rajah" silk, her hair shone at its most silvery, her soft cheeks so often gray from pain and unhappiness were pink with excitement. They shook hands.

"Why, Archie, what a magnificent mustache!"

She didn't *really* like it. I knew *that* but he seemed pleased and they broke into spontaneous laughter, exactly as Phoebe and I did when there was a secret joke between us.

"D'ye like it, Lizzie? I grew it just for you, y'know."

What an atrocious lie!

"Really? How delightful of you!" and they laughed again.

What was this? I thought they hated each other. Here they were enjoying each other's company. It was like looking through a stereopticon for the first time; another dimension to my mother's personality sprang into focus. To see her this way, no longer *my* mother, but someone who had once belonged to another world from mine, my father's world, provoked in me a peculiar mixture of joy and resentment.

Then he glanced at me.

"Hello, Amanda," he said matching my grave look. Dutifully I put up my cheek and bending slightly he gave me a perfunctory kiss. "How are you?"

"I'm very well. How are you?" I replied unsmilingly. I didn't like my smile because my teeth stuck out and I wasn't sure I liked him. His eyes narrowing a trifle he studied my face to see if I were being impertinent.

"I'm well," he said with a short now mirthless laugh that dismissed me. Then turning to Mother he spoke brusquely, "My God, Lizzie! Don't tell me you're still using that stuff. What's it called? That powder?"

This *was* amazing with the rooms still cold from being aired all day until a few minutes before his arrival; the awkward silence from all four of us must have signaled to him for he said, quickly resuming his former insouciance: "Heavens knows, Lizzie, you don't *look* sick. You're as beautiful as ever. How do you do it?"

Mother didn't answer, only flushed and gazed beyond him, as she had a habit of doing when she was deep in thoughts of her own.

"But, Father, she has to smoke it so she won't breathe," Phoebe explained looking up at him earnestly and everyone welcomed the chance to laugh, even I, though I knew Phoebe knew better.

Then Father caught Phoebe up and began roughhousing with her, Rachel joining in the fun while I stood in the background, yearning to be part of it but uncertain of how to go about it until Mother drew me to her side and put her arm around me.

"Now boys," said Father—he always called us "boys" or "old socks"—"what about that walk? Come on! On the double!" and we set off down the stairs and into the raw December afternoon, Father walking so fast we had trouble keeping up with him, especially Phoebe whose legs were still short. I thought he walked fast so he wouldn't have to talk; if there was anything he hated it was having to make conversation.

We walked four times around the same block, not to Divinity Field where Rachel and I had wanted to go, there wasn't time for that, then back to our house where Mother had her best tea things laid out. She and Rachel had taken them down that morning from the top shelf in the little corner china closet and Rachel had washed off the thick dust and carefully dried them.

"Your father will be pleased," Mother had told her. "He likes things to be neat and clean."

Father drank his tea quickly and refused the chocolate cake I had been sent to the corner store to buy. Everything he did was always in a hurry as if he must rush through whatever he was about in order to get on to whatever was next on his program.

"I've got to catch the five o'clock back to New York," he announced and was about to take his leave when Mother hastily interposed.

"I'd like to talk to you for a minute, Archie. Girls, would you go to your rooms and play for a while. I'd like to speak to your father."

We complied instantly. We knew what she had to say. Their voices faint but perfectly audible floated down the narrow corridor leading to Phoebe's and my bedroom, Mother's low urgent tone: ". . . have to have something now or . . ."

". . . quite impossible at the moment," curtly from Father. No flirting or flattery now.

"But I can't wait!" in a ringing tone from Mother. "We'll be out on the street if I don't have something right away!"

Something from Father about the "old doctor" and Mother: "No! I cannot and *will* not ask Father for anything more. He's done far too much as it is."

"Very well, I'll make out a check for the rent, but that's *all* I can do right now. I've told you before, Lizzie, and you'll just have to believe me—I'm doing the *very* best I can."

"You have enough money to take that woman to the opera." Mother's voice was cold and angry.

Then there was a blur of both voices followed by Father's: ". . . if you didn't insist on living in the city you

could have a nice little house in one of the suburbs for half
..."

"Never!" passionately from Mother. "I'll *never* move to
the country! What kind of public schools for your daughters do you think I'd find in the country?"

". . . if it's what you want" was all I could catch of his
rejoinder, and: "but I don't know how you can stand this
kind of life . . ."

"And how do you stand the life *you're* leading!" Mother
burst out angrily. I knew she was hurt that he should cast
aspersions on our surroundings. "How can *any* man,"
Mother went on, "who has one *grain* of decency or honor
stand such a life!"

At this there was a sound of a chair being pushed
roughly back and my father's voice, angry now too and
haughty: "When are you ever going to learn, Eliza, that I
am not *any* man? I never *have* been and *no* one, not even
you, is going to make me behave as if I were!"

Then Mother's voice low and deadly, each word clearly
enunciated: "Have no fear, Archibald Willard. Have no
fear. *I'll* never again try to make you do anything. All I ask
is that you support your family, according to the terms of
the agreement. As for the rest you can *be* what you will.
I've given up long ago trying to help you."

"You're very bitter, Lizzie."

"Yes, I'm bitter." Mother's voice sounded weary and sad
now. "Wouldn't you be bitter if *your* whole life had been
wrecked? Everything you cared about smashed to pieces?"

He made no reply to this and after a few more moments
he said abruptly: "I'm going to miss that *train*. I *must* go."
Then in his former hearty voice he was calling out to us,
"Goodbye boys!" and we dashed back to the living room.

A moment more and he was gone as quickly as he had
come. Once he had departed I forgot about him. It was as
if a window shade had dropped down between me and my

thoughts of him. I did not want to have to think about him any more than was absolutely necessary.

But Mother couldn't drop the shade as easily. When he had gone and she had taken off her pretty blouse and put on her faded blue wrapper, her youthful gaiety vanished and she seemed sadder and older than ever before. After Phoebe was asleep that night, as I lay listening to Mother and Rachel talking in the living room, I knew all at once that Mother was crying. Springing out of bed I ran down the hall to the living room and put my arms around her.

"What is it, Mother? What is it?"

"Oh, Mandy dear, you and Rachel and Phoebe are such a comfort to me, such a comfort."

"What happened?" I cried. "What did he say to you?"

"He didn't say anything, but you may as well know, Mandy, he gave me only twenty-five dollars, *twenty-five dollars!* to pay the rent and food—and Bridget—I won't be able to keep Bridget on what he's giving me. As it is the poor girl's not getting a proper wage—I'm afraid she's going to leave us." And she closed her eyes and put her hand to them as if her head ached terribly.

"What shall we do, Mother?" Rachel chewed her finger-nails savagely until Mother put out her hand to stop her. "Can Grandpa Evans give you some money?"

"No, dear, no, I can't ask Grandpa for anything more— not right now—he's having money troubles of his own. I don't know. I just *don't* know." She shook her head and stared into the distance. Then turning to Rachel and me standing there in our long flannel nightgowns she smiled suddenly and stretched a hand to each of us. "I'll find a way somehow," she said briskly drawing us to her chair. "Don't worry. I always have, haven't I?" We nodded solemnly. "Yes—and God will look out for us. Grandpa Evans is right. We must have faith in God. And we must have charity. The Bible says 'faith, hope and charity, but the greatest of these is charity'. That means love. The Bible used to *say* 'love' but they changed it to charity because the world 'love' was misused and came to mean carnal rather than spiritual love." Then somberly, "But don't forget, my girls, your father has done us all a great wrong, a very great wrong. All that charm—oh yes—but *no*, I can never, *never* take him back!"

We were silent for a moment. Then Rachel spoke. "Did he—did Father ask you to take him back?"

"Not this time but he has in the past—many times . . ."

There was a tremor to her voice. How strange! Was she disappointed that he hadn't? As if she read my thoughts she turned to me. "No, I can never take him back, never, never."

A sound of bare feet thudding in the hall and Phoebe appeared, her hair tousled, her eyes blinking from the sudden bright light. "What is it, Mother? Has Father been mean to you?"

"It's all right, darling, it's all right," Mother said holding out a hand to her. "Come, girls, we haven't said our prayers tonight."

So we knelt down and repeated together The Lord's Prayer and Mother added: "God bless us all and help Mother and Rachel and Amanda and Phoebe to be good for the sake of Jesus Christ our Lord, Amen."

READING ALOUD

From the time when we were very little children Mother spent many hours reading aloud to us. My earliest memory of her reading is *Treasure Island* when I was six or seven, the part where old blind Pew taps with his stick along the frozen road to the Admiral Benbow Inn, then grips Jim Hawkins' arm with his viselike fingers, or where Jim in the apple barrel, his heart hammering in his ears, listens to Old Silver and the other pirates plotting their evil plans. My heart hammers now when I reread these passages. The dramatic ring of my mother's voice is with me again and the frightening glances she darted at us.

That winter on Wellington Street she was reading us *King Lear*, her favorite play, probably because she identified herself with Cordelia. She too was one of three daughters and her father's favorite. She couldn't wait to share it with us, unfortunately for Phoebe who was too young to enjoy it and used to fall asleep, while Rachel and I raced along almost abreast of Mother, welling with indignation at Goneril and Regan for their treatment of the poor mad old man wandering through the storm, his white hair tossed by the winds. She didn't read the play in its entirety, or *I* never could have endured; in fact she seldom finished anything she read, just dipped in and took the parts she found the most appealing, then moved rapidly on to something else leaving us to finish it, sometimes years later.

Nor did she confine us to Shakespeare. Her method of reading allowed her to fit a score of books into one winter.

We had patches of Dickens, *Oliver Twist, Nicholas Nickelby, Dombey and Son;* Thackeray, *Vanity Fair, Henry Esmond, The Rose and the Ring* (which she did finish because we all three insisted); Mark Twain; George Eliot; and reams of J. M. Barrie.

Maude Adams had been her idol both as Peter Pan and as Babbie in *The Little Minister.* As she read she would pause to describe just how Maude Adams had looked, the exact tone and quality of her voice as she read her lines, the costumes she had worn (Babbie with the red berries in her hair). We heard too about Minnie Maddern Fiske, a "fascinating Becky Sharp in brilliant green," and Rawdon Crawley, played by Maurice Barrymore, in purple evening dress, a satin-lined cloak slung across one shoulder.

But no one could touch Bernhardt's performance in *Hamlet* or in *L'Aiglon.* "She held her audience with one finger," Mother told us in ringing tones, holding up her own finger to illustrate and fixing us with a fierce eye.

It was as if she were right up on the stage playing the scene when Mother read aloud. Her eyes threw off blue sparks, her voice trembled as she recited her favorite lines: "How sharper than a serpent's *tooth* is it to have a thankless child!" or "But this above *all,* first to thine own *self* be true and it shall follow as the night the day, thou canst not then be false to *any* man!"

FAMILY STORIES

In the evenings when she was reading aloud Mother would often lapse into stories about her family and childhood and about Father.

Father's childhood though luxurious was not a happy one. His father he had hardly known; his mother had always found him difficult even as a small boy; Thomas, the younger son, was her favorite; at an early age he was sent off to boarding school in New Hampshire, where having spent less than a term, he was expelled for unruly behavior and then, because the schools in Maine were not considered up to the promise of this "brilliant youth" and because his mother was too "delicate" to cope with him, he was sent to live with his Aunt Hester, a maiden lady, in Norwell, Massachusetts.

Here he attended public high school where my mother, just graduated from Radcliffe College, was teaching English. Gay and high spirited, she was very popular with her students, had introduced the teaching of ballroom dancing, the waltz, the polka, the schottische, a sensational innovation in those days, and was that year engaged in putting on *The Pirates of Penzance*. With his lean good looks and pleasant tenor voice Father was a natural for the part of Frederick.

Although Mother was too modest to say so, it was evident from the stories interspersed with her happy chuckling laugh that all the boys including my father were in love with her. Her favorite anecdote about Father and herself was of the time when he was misbehaving in her class and she finally dismissed him for a period of two weeks, an unprecedented action on the part of a teacher. She was fearful that the principal might not back her up, or that Father, a headstrong youth, might never return to her classroom. Of course it all turned out well, as did all of her stories about her teaching days. When the morning came for his return the English teacher stood anxiously at her desk.

"I kept my eye on the big clock over the blackboard. The other students were all in their places. I was afraid he wasn't coming and that I had lost the day, but just as the big black hand reached nine, in strode Archibald, head up, eyes staring straight ahead. He had been waiting in the corridor until the very last moment. It must have taken a lot to get him to make up his mind. It was the first time in his life, I'm sure, that anyone had ever been able to *make* him do *anything*. He was very proud and *very* stubborn. But he couldn't bear to stay away any longer, he told me afterward. He loved English so much. And we were reading *Hamlet*, his favorite play. So without a word or a look he marched to his desk and sat down and from that moment *on* never again did he misbehave in my classroom!"

When he left Norwell to go to school in England for a year before entering Harvard College he had said to her: "Eliza Evans, I'm coming back some day and you're going to marry me!"

"I laughed at him," she told us wryly, "but six years later he did come back," and in a whirlwind courtship they were married. "He swept me off my feet," she said.

Mother's childhood was a happier one than Father's. The next to the youngest of five children she was her father's favorite. "Lizzie darlin'" he always called her (though she thoroughly disliked the nickname and only allowed him and my father to use it). She remembered her youth as "jolly" and told us many stories about their happy times in the big five-storied house on Westminster Avenue.

Grandpa Evans would never move from there and by the time he was an old man the once fashionable neighborhood had become a slum peopled mostly by Negroes, the fine old brownstone next door to Grandpa's now bearing a flashing neon sign, DINING ROOM, the once charming park across the way dingy and brown and bisected by the elevated railway.

This park with its little fountain in the center was the feature of another story. Mother and two of her classmates at the Girls Latin School had equally high marks in their senior year. The teacher in order to select one as valedictorian had asked them to write an essay, the best one to be awarded the coveted distinction, the essay to be used as the valedictory address. Mother told how, walking home from school, day after day searching her mind for an original idea, she noticed the little fountain steadily playing its small stream and was suddenly struck with the thought that, as a symbol of posterity, it might be a fitting subject for her composition. So she wrote it and won the prize and gave the valedictory address.

Her years at Radcliffe were happy ones. She took an active part in Idler, the college dramatic society, and loved to tell stories about herself in various dramatic roles. In those days college centered around the girls and their professors with little emphasis on young men, but her holidays were filled with parties and balls; she had kept a few of her ball dresses, several pairs of small white kid gloves and one pair of tiny white satin slippers with large bows and French heels.

Although her family were not in society they had many friends. Their summer sojourns at the Marshall House, in York Harbor, Maine, were full of picnics, charades, dances, and "jolly" times. She liked to describe one occasion at the big house on Westminster Avenue when her father, who was very "lavish with us children," had whole boughs of mountain laurel brought from the country at outrageous expense to decorate the entire downstairs, and how they had come down, all five of them, two boys and three girls, in their evening regalia, and had stood in a row looking and laughing at themselves in the wallsized mirror flanking the staircase.

"Our friends said coming to the Evans house was *always* like going to a party," she told us.

After Radcliffe she had taught for a year at a small private school in Fitchburg, Massachusetts, then to Norwell where she boarded with a nice old couple on a farm (they remained her friends until they died). Mother was proud of her "gumption" in getting out and earning her own living; she and her sisters were brought up by their father in the feminist tradition to believe they could manage their lives as well as any man. He insisted that all three go to college and prepare themselves for a career.

"We were much ahead of our time," Mother told us. "People used to be shocked at us because we didn't wear corsets and long petticoats and corset covers and what not, but Father said corsets were bad for our health. My sister Belle made up a little verse about us:

> *'No corsets for us,*
> *No trailing in the dirt,*
> *A chemmy's what* we *wear,*
> *And a pettiskirt.'*

"We had such fun in our family," Mother told us. "None of us was in the slightest hurry to get married."

It was to this big jolly family that Father, presumably a rather lonely young man, was introduced soon after his return to America. After school in England he had gone to Harvard where in the space of three years he had received his bachelor's degree and his master's degree in English literature, a record achievement even at that time; after that, being a young man of many talents, he had spent two years in Paris studying painting.

He and Mother were married by a justice of the peace; a religious service was out of the question he being an avowed atheist and unwilling to set foot in a church even for a wedding.

Both families were opposed to the match but he was determined, "Once Archie Willard makes up his mind nothing on heaven or earth can stop him", and although she never admitted it, Mother herself must have had grave misgivings. Great Aunt Hester, Grandmother Willard's sister, who seemed to know more about family matters than anyone else told me years later: "Your mother gave her solemn promise to my sister, Victoria, that since both of them agreed the union was unsuitable, she would *never* marry her son. Three weeks later Eliza Evans broke her word!"·

However often I questioned her as to why such a promise had been extracted or given, Great Aunt Hester's only rejoinder was a folding of her lips, a shake of her head, and the dour words: "Eliza Evans broke her word to my sister three weeks after she gave it. I know a good deal more beside but that's all I shall say."

According to the standards of their time my father and mother were far from a conventional couple. During their brief courtship they used to breakfast together in various restaurants in Harvard Square before Mother went off on the trolley to her teaching. They played chess throughout the meal, a game at which both of them excelled.

The story we children liked the best was the one about their honeymoon, a canoe trip in the wilds of Maine with

Father's best friend, Jerry Merrill, and his younger brother, Thomas.

"Some women might not relish a honeymoon with two other men," Mother told us laughing, "but I liked it. Archie always did unusual things—and the boys were very kind to me."

On this trip Mother had a violent attack of asthma, but she refused to give up and return home. When the three men portaged from one river to another she was so weak that she had to be carried along with the canoe.

"Your father had a gift for getting everyone to work. He assigned duties to each of us and mine, when I had got my strength back, was to sit in the middle of the canoe and read Edgar Allen Poe aloud. Archie was very keen about his poetry. The men took turns paddling, bow and stern, the third one sitting in the middle of the canoe holding a parasol over my head to keep the sun out of my eyes while I read. Each one could hardly wait to do his part until he discovered how tedious it was—sitting for an hour on end holding up that parasol."

Mother related all this with such indulgent amusement and wealth of detail that even as a small girl I had a clear picture of this strange honeymoon—the brilliant dashing youth and his two friends, in their midst the fascinating young woman.

Certainly my parents had a good deal in common. Both of them were extraordinarily versatile. Equally brilliant in her college years at English, languages, and mathematics, Mother excelled in dramatics, music, and dancing. Father, a capable sportsman, talented as a painter, with a pleasing tenor voice, was also according to Mother a mechanical genius.

Mother often spoke proudly of how creative, how original Father was, but always in the past tense. His paintings when she had first married him had been "sensitive," "poignant," "whimsical"; now they were "immoral," "degenerate," "disgusting expressions of free love, that *curse of our generation!*" "With their horrible bloated bodies with heavy lines, they look for all the world like something out of the comic strips!" He would do better to give up painting entirely if he had to create such "outrages."

The most dramatic of Mother's stories were those about the war years in London. Soon after I was born, Father, who had had to abandon painting as a career and take up a more practical occupation for a man with a wife and two children to support, had succeeded through family connections in obtaining a position in an advertising firm in London. After he had been there a few months, he wrote to Mother urging her to join him, and in March of 1914 she had sailed over with her two babies.

We had lived in London for almost two years, in a flat in Highbury Barn, where Phoebe was born on May 7, 1915, the night the *Lusitania* went down.

"Think of it, girls over a thousand men, women, and children lost their lives on that ship!" Mother told us, "Sunk by a German submarine with *no* warning! Everyone was up in arms! You've no idea the excitement in London that day—all over the world for that matter . . . and there I was alone in London with my three babies! Your father had returned to the States to look for another position—he couldn't wait until Phoebe came. The German zeppelins were dropping bombs in England all through that winter and spring, and we never knew from one minute to the next whether they would get to London. Every night I lay awake planning and worrying about how I would ever get home. I couldn't get any decent help over there. The wonderful trained nurse, who had been with me all through Phoebe's birth, had to leave me to go to France to nurse the wounded soldiers . . ."

She told us how she tried all through the summer of

1915 to get back to America. "The German U Boats were in home waters laying mines and torpedoing English and even American ships . . . Twice I arranged return passage for us and *both* times I was warned in a dream not to sail, that the ship would be torpedoed! So I canceled passage and they *were* torpedoed without any warning and with a loss of many lives!"

The third time she arranged passage she had had no dream so we sailed as planned, my mother, Rachel, Phoebe and I, "three babies in arms," she always said, and a very young nurse she had managed to corral at the last moment, who was both homesick and seasick throughout the voyage. But we came safely home at last.

"People ask me how I ever lived through it," she told us, "and sometimes I wonder how I did, but in those days, girls, though you might not believe it now, I had my health and strength—and *plenty* of courage!"

THE SEPARATION AGREEMENT

Just before the Christmas holidays that winter at Mrs. Ryan's house we were awakened earlier than usual one morning by the long piercing no-school whistle, a happily familiar sound. Hugging my knees and shivering, I sat up in bed and gazed out of the window for a moment at Mrs. Ryan's pocket-handkerchief garden transformed, the pear tree, grape arbor, and shrubs shrouded and lumpish under the heavy snow. It was a blizzard! I shouted to Phoebe. With a whoop she was in my bed pressing her nose against the cold pane, then burrowing happily under the warm quilt.

We didn't wait lazily this morning until Bridget had started the coal fire in the kitchen, but bounded out of bed and into the bathroom where Mother had already lighted the oil stove. (The central heating in our flat was feeble, Mother said, because Mrs. Ryan saved on coal.)

After a hasty breakfast of hot porridge, we three girls hurried into our outdoor clothes: over our long underwear voluminous pleated serge bloomers and long woolen stockings, heavy Shaker-knit sweaters, tam o'shanters, mittens, and black felt overshoes buckled over our high-laced boots. So clumsy we could scarcely waddle and overcome with fits of laughter at our bulky costumes, we plunged downstairs and out into Mrs. Ryan's backyard.

The first thing of course was to lie flat on our backs in the heavenly stuff and make angels; then it was snowballs, tremendous ones, then snowmen. After an hour or so of this, thoroughly wet and cold, we retreated upstairs to Mother and Bridget to spread our things by the coal fire and sip hot cocoa.

In the afternoon when the snow was packed and shining like porcelain we set forth with Mother's permission for Sach's hill. It was a beautiful afternoon—no longer snowing. The sun had come out, the sky was brilliant blue; the unbelievable fairyland of the morning was fast melting away.

The pungs were busy on their afternoon rounds. Rachel and Phoebe and I were able to hop onto the back of a coal pung without the driver catching sight of us. If he had he would surely have shouted at us to get off and even flicked his whip in our direction. What pleasure to glide smoothly along, our overshoes firmly planted on the runners, with the snorts and puffs of the tired horse, the bells on his harness and the sharp "giddups" and "geehaws" of the driver mingling in our ears.

The big white house that stood on the other side of the high wooden fence, once the Charles Eliot Norton estate, now belonged to Professor Sachs of Harvard College. Everyone went coasting there, rich and poor, Shady Hill-ites and those on the other side of the fence, even the "Somerville Bums."

That afternoon, our first one there, Rachel and Phoebe and I were a trifle daunted. The big tough boys from Somerville alarmed us with their wild ways. Running with their heavy boots, along the slippery crest, yelling at the tops of their hoarse voices, then crashing headlong onto their battered sleds "belly bumps," their lank hair falling over their sparsely bearded faces, soiled and wet with snow, sweat and unheeded snot, they bore down on the girls in their path swerving to miss them only by a hair at the last instant.

The Somerville girls, some of them as big and rough as the boys, others delicate with an unhealthy pallor under their heavily rouged cheeks, stood shivering in their pitifully thin jackets and tight short skirts only pretending, it seemed, to be frightened when the boys bombarded them with rocklike snowballs or tossed them brutally onto the snow. They appeared not to care a bit about the coasting, merely to be waiting for these attacks, when they would scream with shrill laughter or shout curses in high-pitched voices.

But there was something romantic about the atmosphere they created. When Rachel and Phoebe and I, sliding sedately down a side path on our Flexible Flyer, our overshoes neatly tucked into each other's laps, were overcome by a sledload of "toughs" hurtling past us singing boisterously, "Wherever you go, whatever you do, why all of the time I'm folleyin' you," a thrill of excitement streaked through me.

We soon forgot them, however, in the undiluted enjoyment of scrambling up and rocketing down the steeper sections of the hill. The hours disappeared. Before we realized it darkness was upon us and we had to run all the way home through Divinity Field banging our sled behind us, convinced there must be "degenerates" (as Grandpa Evans called them) lurking behind every tree.

The next day, the start of our Christmas vacation, Rachel set off for her annual Christmas visit to my Grandmother Willard and Mother began to fret as she always did at this time of year. It had been written into the separation agreement that Rachel was to go to Maine for a week directly before Christmas to be with my grandmother and my father, who traveled all the way from New York City to be with his mother and his eldest daughter. Sometimes Phoebe and I spent a few days in the summer, when we were invited, but these visits depended on my grandmother's wishes; we had not been included in the separation agreement.

Every year as Christmas approached Mother talked for hours about the past. That evening after Rachel had been put on the train at North Station and Bridget had gone to the moving pictures with her fella she told us all about it again. She and Phoebe and I, in our wrappers and bedslippers, were in the kitchen having supper, Gorton's "ready-to-fry" codfish cakes and homemade apple pie, a special treat, to cheer us up, Mother said. Although, like many young women from well-to-do families of their generation, the Evans sisters had been brought up never to "set foot" in the kitchen, Mother was an excellent cook when she put her mind to it (Father had taught her how to make apple pie when they were first married, using a broom handle to roll out the dough); but each year she seemed to care less about it. Many of our meals now came from cans.

The trouble had all started with Thomas's tragic death, a few days before his twenty-fourth birthday and just one year before Aunt Belle's death. How strange it was, I often thought, that these two deaths, one on each side of the family, marked the downward turn in my parents' lives.

It was in June when Rachel was just four years old that Father and Uncle Thomas and Jerry Merrill had gone off on another of their famous canoe trips.

"They were paddling in very treacherous 'white water'," Mother recalled, "and somehow the canoe was overturned and Uncle Thomas was swept downstream. Before your father could get to him—and he was a powerful swimmer—Thomas's golden head went under for the third time and he was drowned. It nearly killed Archie. When they finally recovered the body, he couldn't bear to look at it. He was so upset he wouldn't even go to the funeral. 'I can't do it, Lizzie,' he said; '*you* go for me,' and the tears were running down his face. It was one of the few times I ever saw him cry. So I went. It was a beautiful service." Mother's upper lip tightened as it always did when she was upset. "Sometimes I think this may have been the reason for all our troubles—Thomas's death—dying like that— did something to your father. It warped him, made him bitter against everyone, man and God. He never set foot in a church again and heaven knows he'd been atheist enough before it happened. It was right after that that he—" She broke off and closed her eyes for a moment. "I think he loved Thomas more than anyone in the world."

"More than he loved you? And us?" I asked.

"It was different. You see, he'd known him longer. Thomas was the only person he was close to when he was a child. His father was dead and no one can be close to his mother. She isn't capable of loving anyone really except herself."

"What happened then?" I prompted. I knew she wanted to tell the story all over again and I liked hearing it except for the parts about Grandmother Willard. Phoebe and I were bored with those. But she wasn't to be put off so easily.

"I don't know how—with that woman for a mother—he could have been, but your Uncle Thomas was one of the sweetest people I've ever known. Everyone loved him. I loved him. He was very good to me. I thank God he didn't live to know what's happening to me—and my little Rachel. How he loved that little girl! She was there at Pinewood so much, of course—he knew her better than he did you younger girls. He used to hang over her crib for hours playing with her and singing to her. He'd always wanted a baby sister, he told me once, and now he had one. Poor Thomas!"

"I wish I'd known him," put in Phoebe. "He sounds awful nice."

"Awful*ly* nice, dear. An *adverb* modifies an adjective— and 'awful' is too strong a word in any case. It means to inspire awe. Better to say 'very' or 'exceedingly'. We weaken our language by using powerful words when mild ones will do. Yes, he was very nice and you," smiling at Phoebe, "are very like him, the same brown eyes and golden hair. If you have a boy, I hope you will name him Thomas. I don't know though," sighing, "I suppose it might be bad luck for a child to bear that name."

"What about Rachel?" I urged.

"Well, then after his death, your grandmother, as you know, had a sort of nervous breakdown. She was crazy with grief naturally. Who wouldn't be losing that beautiful boy? And she'd lost her husband too when she was a very young woman, though I don't think she ever loved him—

the way she did Thomas. Anyway I felt sorry for her. She asked me to let her keep Rachel for a while. Rachel had been there a great deal. I'd been sick off and on ever since I'd got back from London—sick and worn out with too many babies too soon. So I let her keep Rachel for six months! And that was when the fatal seed was planted—to take Rachel away from me! Oh my God! Why did I ever let her do it?"

"But Rachel only goes there part of the time" I objected. "She doesn't *live* there."

"Yes, only part of the time—but soon—very *soon,* mark my word, Amanda, it will be *all* the time!" Her tone was low, her eyes looked beyond me as if she were gazing into the distant future.

"What do you mean?" This was new to me.

"Yes," Mother went on solemnly, "the agreement states in black and white that at such time in the course of her education as seems fitting Rachel will be sent off to a boarding school of her *grandmother's choice*—Oh how could I ever have let those weasel words get by me?—and at her expense. And when that time *comes* that Rachel goes to a school of *her* choosing she will be gone from *me* forever!" She paused, one eyebrow lifted dramatically.

"But why?" I said.

"Because, don't you see, that woman will choose a school near Wychmere of course, not a school near *here.* Oh no! And I let her do it, God forgive me!" and she put her mouth in her hand and pressed her cheeks very hard with her fingers.

"But you couldn't help it!" cried Phoebe running to Mother and putting her arms around her neck. Mother patted Phoebe's hand.

"Yes, Phoebe, I could have helped it, but I was young then and idealistic. I wanted to do the right thing for your grandmother. I felt so desperately sorry for her," she sighed heavily, "and I was worn out with worry and illness and small children and everything else. Your father was behaving badly, very badly. But I'm not going into all that. You children have had enough of a burden without hearing any more of *that* sordid business."

"But why *was* he with all those women?" I insisted.

"I don't know, Amanda, I *don't* know—to satisfy his ego, I guess. Your father is an egoist, a complete egoist."

"What's an egoist?" said Phoebe.

"An egoist is a self-centered person, different from an ego*t*ist which means a conceited person—your father isn't that—but he *is* self-centered—the most self-centered person I've *ever* known except his mother."

"So then what happened?" I said.

"Two years later when it finally came about that I had to make up my mind to leave him for good—I'd taken him back and *taken* him back—and it was no use—he came to me the day of the signing of the agreement and *begged* me with tears in his eyes to let his mother have Rachel part of the time so he could go there to visit and be with her. So they persuaded me. They said your grandmother was ill and that I should be charitable. Her sister, Hester, who's a better person than the rest of that family, said it would be the only salvation for her. So I let them do it. I let them take my little girl away that very summer. I was weak. Oh God! How could I have been so weak!" and Phoebe and I thought she would cry. She always did when she told this part but instead she suddenly grew very angry, her lips tightened, her eyes burned right into us. "Oh God! How I hate that woman! God forgive me but I can't help it! I blame her for what she did to your father and now she will have Rachel, a young impressionable child!"

"But how *can* she take Rachel away from us?" I protested. I could never see the logic to this fear of Mother's. "She's your child, not Grandmother Willard's."

"Ah, Amanda, that's the terrible part of it. There's nothing I can do against her. She's the powerful one."

"But why? Why aren't you powerful?"

She looked at me with that strange look of hers that always made a shiver go through me.

"Money, Amanda!" Phoebe and I stared at her. "Yes. Terrible as it may seem, *money* is power in this vale of misery."

"But why can't she *help* Rachel if she has money?" I suggested.

"Perhaps she can. I hope to *heaven* she will. But she has a dark side to her, an evil side. Little do you know, Amanda, how evil she can be."

"She doesn't *seem* evil," I argued. "She just seems cross."

Mother's eyes blazed threateningly. "She's evil! Make no mistake about that, Amanda Willard! She's what her own cousin, Rachel Stuart, said about her—a drop of poison in the cup! Oh, Amanda, little do you know what she's capable of doing—what she's already done!"

"What has she done?" I said.

"The Bible says to forgive our enemies. You'll never know how many times I've gone down on my knees and asked God to help me to be forgiving, but I can *never* forget what she did—how she betrayed me!"

"You mean taking Rachel away?" It was difficult for Phoebe to understand these things.

"No, I mean *betrayed* me—after I had signed my child away to her, for *her* sake and her son's sake—she turned on me, said terrible things behind my back about me, tried to turn my *own* family against me—and I *trusted* her."

"I wish—" Phoebe began, "I wish—that you and Father —and Grandmother—would like each other," and she burst into a shudder of sobbing and ran to throw herself into Mother's arms.

"Oh my poor little Phoebe," Mother said. "God forgive

me for telling you, poor baby, about these things—and you too, my Mandy. Oh, I shouldn't tell you these things. You're too young, but . . ."

"But I *like* to hear about things," I said. "Phoebe may be too young but I'm not."

"No, Mandy," Mother said smiling at me, "you're old for your years. Heaven knows you and Rachel have had to be. But now, girls," and her tone became brisk and cheerful, "we've been gloomy long enough. Let's do something jolly to cheer us up. What would you like? Shall we play cards or shall we go on with *Oliver Twist?*

"Oliver! Oliver!" We said both at once. And so while I washed the dishes and Phoebe wiped them, Mother read aloud to us our favorite book.

CHRISTMAS

Christmas was by far the biggest event in our year. Mother always gave us nice presents and my Grandfather Willard's brother, Great Uncle Ezekial, was particularly generous to his dead brother's grandchildren. Uncle Zeke, as we called him, was the only member of the Millwood Willards we knew. He used to come once a year with his wife, Aunt Emmeline, to pay us a call in an enormous black limousine with what I always imagined was a white marble running board, driven by their Negro chauffeur in uniform. Uncle

Zeke called himself "Dr. Sawdust" and used to bring us children lollipops for "medicine."

When they arrived all the kids in the neighborhood would crowd around to gape at the big car, the smartly dressed chauffeur, and the oddly dressed couple, Uncle Zeke in a Chesterfield with a mink collar, a derby hat, wearing a monocle, and carrying a silver-headed cane, Aunt Emmeline with brilliant gold hair (though she must have been close to seventy) in long flowing wraps crowned with enormous hats trailing veils of mauve or chartreuse.

Mother was pleased with these attentions from Uncle Zeke—"a charming generous man—your Grandfather Willard must have been so like him," she would say. My father's presents were never as well received as his uncle's. "His secretary must have picked *that* out—Archie would never have chosen it—he *does* have good taste when he bothers to spend the time" was the usual comment.

This Christmas as always Uncle Zeke's presents arrived well beforehand carefully marked "Do not open until Christmas," and Rachel returned as always on Christmas Eve brimming with news and bearing all sorts of marvelous secrets.

My grandmother was a clever and painstaking seamstress and used to make us lovely things. I particularly remember the flannel petticoats neatly featherstitched in pure white silk thread set off by the yellow of the flannel. Girls' underwear in those days was an elaborate affair: long woolen union suits from neck to ankle "ninety percent wool," cotton waists with two rows of yellow buttons, the lower one for our white cotton drawers, the upper for our petticoats, in cold weather two of them, flannel underneath, white ruffled cotton on top.

Grandmother Willard made most of Rachel's clothes and sometimes made things for Phoebe and me which Mother considered "too fussy." Mother made dresses for all three of us. She would cut them out three or six at a time from one pattern—her boast was she could "run up" three in a day—always with straight lines with wide plain sleeves, made of Anderson gingham or "aeroplane linen." Their only decoration was a black or red patent leather belt. Mother admired simplicity in clothes but I secretly preferred my grandmother's puff sleeved, smocked, and beribboned frocks.

When still a little girl Rachel had learned from Grandmother Willard how to sew, knit, and crochet. Precocious to start with, she had in effect two mothers to encourage her talents. Mother saw to it that she had piano lessons as long as she could afford them, Grandmother Willard gave her ballet and French lessons during the summer; from her she also learned about flowers and birds, from Mother about English literature. Each woman was jealous of the other's influence. My grandmother, though she had had little formal schooling, was well read and oddly she and Mother had similar tastes in literature. Sometimes the rivalry was so excessive it was comical. Rachel would go to Maine enthusiastic about *David Copperfield* and return saying *Great Expectations* was a finer novel. Mother would say this was poppycock and *David Copperfield* would be reinstated until the next visit, when *Vanity Fair* and *Henry Esmond* were on the list.

As soon as she was safely out of the taxi, Rachel hurried into her room to hide the bundles away until the next morning. After our favorite supper of baked beans and brown bread Mother read us "T'was the night before Christmas." Though we knew it by heart we liked to hear it every Christmas, and then Phoebe and I were sent jumping with excitement to bed, where we lay awake for what seemed hours listening for the sound of Santa's sleighbells. Just before I fell off I heard Mother saying something about that "unprincipled woman" so I knew she meant my

Grandmother Willard, but that was all I could catch; then Rachel's clear voice: "But, Mother, she was very kind, really she was."

The next morning we had our stockings and right after breakfast our presents, which we opened in front of the little tree Bridget had bought. Uncle Zeke had given Rachel a tiny gold ring and Phoebe and myself each a doll, mine a china one with real hair, just what I wanted, and Phoebe a Raggedy Ann doll which disappointed her so much that she threw her in her breakfast oatmeal in a fit of temper. Afterward she repented, washed the oatmeal off, wept over her and decided she loved her dearly, all of which caused me to wonder if a china doll *was* what I really wanted.

That was the Christmas Father sent us stockings—six pairs each all just alike—very practical, Mother said, but "hardly exciting for a Christmas present."

After Bridget had left for her home in Brockton for her holiday, we had our chicken (turkey was too big for our oven and too expensive) and then Mother told us Grandpa Evans was going to be able to "steal away" from Uncle James with Albert for an hour and take us for a drive. It was a nice Christmas.

DEATH

Two people we knew died that winter, both very suddenly. One was Miss Baldwin, the Negro principal of the Agassiz School, who had built up such a remarkable reputation. Unfortunately she died during our first year at the school so I hardly remember her, but I remember her funeral and more vividly her corpse for it was the first one I'd ever seen. She had been a tall buxom woman with brilliant eyes, white teeth, and glowing color under her dark skin. I had never thought of her as old but in her coffin she was tiny and shriveled, her lovely brown color wasted to a washed-out gray, her mouth sunken, her face drawn. Whatever it was that had killed her had produced so drastic a change in her appearance it shocked us all; we had seen her only a few weeks before in our school corridors laughing and vibrant.

The other death was more distressing. A family by the name of Kerrigan lived in the upstairs flat of the house next door to Mrs. Ryan's. They were hard-working Irish people with six children and little Helen, aged five, was the darling of the family. She was seized with diphtheria and within a matter of days her death had stunned the neighborhood.

The Kerrigans had a wake of course and Helen's corpse was on display in their front parlor. Mrs. Kerrigan liked my mother. "That Mrs. Willard—she's a lady," she told Mrs. Ryan, so we were invited to come and view "the remains."

I shall never forget my feelings of wonder and curiosity as we tiptoed into the little parlor, darkened and airless, crammed with stiff wreaths and blankets of heavily scented flowers, on the walls a plaster figure of the Virgin Mary, a colored picture of Christ on the cross, his body punctured with wounds, a vermilion heart dripping globules of blood, and in the midst of the moaning women, underneath three flickering candles, the small white casket with its waxlike doll all in white.

PART TWO

12 *Wellington Street*

THE DOUGHERTYS

IN THE SPRING we moved again, to a two-family house two doors away from the Ryans belonging to a family named Dougherty. Mother explained that Mrs. Ryan had become increasingly cranky; "After all, children have to live," she said, and the rent was less at the Doughertys. Except for leaving Mrs. Ryan's garden, Rachel and Phoebe and I were delighted, for the Dougherty family consisted of a father and mother and five children—and Mrs. Dougherty kept a brood of hens and a rooster in their backyard.

School closed that year on Rachel's birthday as usual, and soon after she left by train for her summer visit to my grandmother at Wychmere where she was to spend eight whole weeks this time, in order, as my grandmother had written, that her summer would be a "consecutive period of rest and application to her extracurricular pursuits," which meant her French and ballet lessons.

Mother had not been able to afford Miss Speare's cottage by the lake for us this year and it soon became apparent that, reduced to our own company (most of our friends had gone off somewhere) and the city streets, Phoebe and I were to have a dreary summer. After a good deal of coaxing Mother had allowed us the luxury of going barefoot, and for a while we were happy to wander around the blistering streets pressing tar bubbles with our toes, dressed in our "Tom Sawyers," a combination overall and blouse, which Mother had bought us to play in and which we adored. But this recreation soon palled. Most of all we longed to go swimming but Bridget had been called home for the summer to take care of an ailing aunt, Mother was "down and out" with asthma and we were too young to go alone.

One particularly stifling midsummer morning the entire Dougherty family was setting forth in their "tin lizzie" on an excursion to Mystic Lake in Arlington. Somehow Phoebe and I had understood that we were to be part of this outing and were wild with excitement at the prospect until it became evident that we were not to be included after all. We rushed frantically upstairs to Mother.

"They're not going to take us!" cried Phoebe throwing herself onto Mother's lap and sobbing. I stood by quivering with indignation.

"Take you where, dearie?" said Mother. "What is it all about?"

"About us going to the lake swimming," I put in glumly.

"About *our* going—"

"About our going and Jeanie said last night we could, didn't she, Phoebe?"

"Yes, she did and—oh I think it's so mean—I haven't had one chance to wear my new red bathing suit—"

Phoebe was weeping copiously. I could hardly blame her. I stood there unable to speak with disappointment. Mother sat thinking. I can see her now—in her rocking chair, clad in her grey kimono, one foot tucked under her, a quizzical expression in her eyes, her middle fingernail caught between her teeth.

"Why don't you go down," she said at last, "and just stand quietly by without saying a word and watch them as they get ready . . ."

"But we've been doing that and nothing happens," I argued.

"Well go down again. Perhaps Mrs. Dougherty has been too busy preparing the picnic lunch to think of it."

Such a suggestion was not like Mother who was usually too proud to encourage us to do such a thing—and it didn't work. We went down and stood hungrily watching their every move, as they came and went from kitchen to car, but they set off at last without a backward glance.

To be fair, this was not typical of the Doughertys, a cheerful bouncing family, very friendly and kind to us. Mr. Dougherty, a policeman who used to direct traffic near the Cottage Farm Bridge, was a fine-looking man with bright red cheeks, lovely blue eyes, and prematurely white hair. But Mrs. Dougherty was Mother's favorite, more intelligent than her husband, according to Mother, and "stunning" to look at, though I couldn't see it, a big woman with black hair done in a bun at the back, the same high coloring as Mr. Dougherty and dazzling white teeth. "She has a keen sense of humor," Mother said and "that wonderful Irish wit."

She and Mother used to sit in our flat and have cups of coffee while they talked (Mrs. Dougherty was the only landlady whose company Mother ever enjoyed), and I was frequently allowed to sit with them and have a cup of coffee too. I loved those mornings in our living room listening to the grown-ups talk while my sisters played in the backyard with the Dougherty children. Sometimes I joined them but more often not. I was "delicate" that year, the boys were rough, they would not let me be the leader and if I could not be leader I preferred not to play at all.

Tommy Dougherty, with flaming red hair and freckles (his mother called him an "Irish red devil"), was very poor in his studies, spending most of his school hours throwing spit balls, dipping the pigtails of the girl in front of him in

the ink well, and drawing cartoons of Marietta Mac-
Dougall. Jeanie Dougherty was dark haired and pretty like
her mother, but her teeth were green from never being
brushed. Although a still poorer student than her brother
—she was having a painful time in the first grade learning
to read—she used to steal upstairs in the evenings and
stand at the door listening while Mother read us *Hamlet;*
when discovered she was invited into our living room
where she would sit spellbound while Mother went through
her performance, stimulated by the new audience gazing
wonderingly up at her.

After Jeanie had left, Mother would shake her head and
say: "And they can't teach that child to read!"

THE TRIAL

Very early one bleak November morning, so early it was
dark outside, even the Dougherty's rooster was still asleep,
we three girls were told to get up quietly and get ready to
go to Boston with Mother and Bridget to the Suffolk
County Court House. It was not the first morning we had
been roused early; the trial for the automobile accident
was in its second week now and we had been to court almost every day, but this day was special. Bridget was going
on the stand to testify.

While in our tiny bathroom bathing and dressing by the
warmth of the kerosene stove, the round kind with the

perforated top, I was jostled against it by mistake and my bottom was badly seared. When my outcries had been quieted, the burn carefully dressed by Mother and Bridget and breakfast eaten, Mother gathered us together for one of her little talks.

"Now, girls, this is important, so please listen carefully. I don't want any of you to mention Amanda's burn to anyone, not *anyone*, do you understand? It's a pity it had to happen at all, and to Amanda of all people right at this time, but it will be all right. And I know that you, Mandy, will be my brave girl and bear your pain like a soldier. You will have to sit on your side on the streetcar and in the courtroom and if it hurts too much you can tell Bridget or me and one of us will bring you home. Now let's get on our things and go. This is a *very important day!*"

This lawsuit undertaken by my mother against the Greater Boston Power and Light Company to recover damages suffered by her and by the three of us had been a vital part of our lives for several years now. Mother had explained why it had taken all this time for it to reach trial before a jury. For one thing she had refused to settle out of court for the "absurdly inadequate" sum of money offered us by the Greater Boston Power and Light Company. She had been reading us *Bleak House* that fall so we could understand that anything to do with the law and the courts took many years. It still seemed peculiar to me, however, that the trial should come quite so long after the accident itself.

The accident occurred on Commonwealth Avenue in Boston in the late winter of 1919 when I was seven years old, a year after Father and Mother were separated. All three of us girls had had our tonsils out the day before and were on our way home from the hospital in a taxicab with Mother and a nurse when a Greater Boston Power and

Light Company treasury limousine crashed into us. Mother claimed that the driver of the limousine was drunk.

The taxi spun around in a complete circle, its right door flung open by the impact, and landed against the curbstone. The taxicab driver's nose was broken, Mother had three ribs torn from her backbone, Phoebe was thrown under the taxicab and her head banged against the curb causing a concussion (which was not serious as it turned out but looked horrible—"like a large blue box," Mother said), the nurse was not injured nor was Rachel, but she witnessed the entire proceedings, which made her a "nervous wreck," and I was seriously hurt.

I had insisted on sitting by the window on the left side where the limousine struck. My forehead was so badly cut that the torn flesh was hanging over my face obscuring my left eye. I can clearly remember—I had not lost consciousness—hearing Mother say over and over: "Her eye is gone! Oh my God! Her eye is gone!"

Phoebe couldn't be found anywhere for some time after the initial turmoil and Mother went around frantically crying: "Where's my baby? Where's my baby?" Phoebe was four years old but Mother thought of her as a baby. Finally a woman appeared who had tried to be helpful by removing Phoebe from the frenzied scene into her apartment nearby.

Fortunately this all happened not far from the hospital we had just left. They had to operate on my face five times; in some places the cuts were very deep. We must have had an unusually skillful surgeon, for the scars today are hardly noticeable. The photographs taken of me for the trial are gruesome but I never thought much about it.

"She wears her scars like a sabre cut!" Mother used to say proudly.

The most distressing part of the accident for me was that when I was taken from the hospital at last by Grandpa and

Mother I was made to wear a veil wound around my face and hat like an old woman. How vividly I recollect that morning, driving along the sunny streets, shrinking far back into the cushions of my grandfather's car, praying that no passerby, above all no one my age, could peer into the car and see me in this ignominious headgear.

When the trial began we girls thought what fun it would be to miss so much school, but as the days went on we found it all exceedingly dreary except for occasional recesses when we played on the wide marble-floored corridors of the Suffolk County Court House (the black and white squares were perfect for hopscotch).

Mother had explained from the beginning what the trial was all about. Of course I was the most important person because I had been hurt the most. Ever since the accident I had displayed marked signs of nervous disorder, headaches, backaches, anxiety, extreme nervousness. According to our doctors—general practitioners, surgeons, oculists—the injuries so close to my eyes and my brain were more than enough to account for these nervous disorders. According to the defense, however, it was something quite different. In muted tones and with glinting eyes Mother had told us exactly what the lawyers of the Greater Boston Power and Light Company were up to. They were attempting to prove that there was something wrong with the *whole family* and with me in particular, which was the cause of the trouble with my eyes and my nervousness, and that this *awful* something had nothing whatever to do with the accident but was a result of a loathsome disease in the family! *Inherited!*

We already knew a great deal about syphilis from Grandpa Evans. He specialized in venereal disease and it was one of his favorite topics of conversation. We had often heard him indicate people on the street or patients who had left his office.

"You see that man, children, with his mouth eaten away [or his gait unnatural or his teeth disfigured], that comes from syphilis."

During the course of the trial I was given at least four Wasserman tests and Father and Grandpa Evans, to his righteous indignation, were forced to undergo the same.

Throughout the day that Bridget testified I reclined on my side on the hard bench in the court room and waited for something important to happen, but as far as I could see it was as dreary and uninteresting as ever. To be sure, Bridget did get up on the stand; then they got Rachel up there and even I was taken to the front of the courtroom and stared at by the jury and the judge and the spectators, but I could see nothing *really* interesting or important about any of it.

When we got home that night, however, and Mother explained what it was all about I could see that, for Bridget at least, it had been a red-letter day. It appeared that the defense, in trying to prove that syphilis was the cause of my troubles, had corralled a number of witnesses—various women who had taken care of us children over the years—who would describe the medicines that had been administered to us at the time. That morning when the defense lawyer had finished interrogating a string of nurses and housekeepers, who Mother claimed had been "bought up" by the defense and who testified as to all sorts of ominous-sounding medicines, he put Bridget on the stand and began grilling her.

" 'Please tell the court, Miss McBreen, exactly what medicines Mrs. Willard used for the children during the winter of 1921,' " and Mother jumped up to demonstrate how Mr. Keene, the defense lawyer, had stood and how he had fixed Bridget with his "cruel pale eyes behind those steel spectacles. But Bridget looked straight at the jury and though I knew, Bridgie, you were shaking inside, in a voice as clear as a bell she said 'One bottle of cod liver oil!' Mr. Keene tried to expostulate in vain. The courtroom was rocking with laughter. Even the judge smiled," Mother went on, "and he said to Bridget, 'Young lady, tell us again what medicines were used' and Bridget replied, 'One bottle of cod liver oil!' " Mother loved that story. "It brought the house down," she said.

One afternoon soon after that Mother and I went in town to Mr. Gilpatrick's office (Mother had purposely chosen an Irish Catholic lawyer, "This will be an Irish Catholic jury," she had said), where I was to be examined by several doctors from both sides of the case. Mother had explained to me very carefully before she and I set out on the streetcar why it was all necessary and she was with me throughout the examination but I'll never forget my feelings of embarrassment and outrage standing naked and trembling while three or four doctors and as many lawyers peered at me from top to bottom.

By far the most important witness was my oculist. The outcome of the trial turned on his testimony which proved the fine point that, whereas with syphilis the pupils of the eyes do not contract to light *or* to distance, in my case the pupils did not contract to light *and* to distance.

These details were to Mother fascinating and stimulating but for me they were tedious. I was thoroughly bored with the constant trips to the doctors, the oculist, the lawyer's office. All I wanted was for the whole thing to be over and settled but that was not to be. The settlement was not made until months after the trial and then, the jury having granted us fifty thousand dollars, there was a good deal of talk on the part of the defense about excessive verdicts, the whole thing had to be tried over again, and we came out with considerably less than half that amount.

All this took years. To me the suit was like an ugly shadow, ever present, hovering in the background of our lives. But my mother seemed not to mind these endless postponements and delays; indeed in a strange way she seemed to thrive on it all. This kind of activity seemed to have a great appeal for her.

I never remember her going out in the evening without us children, but often I came home from school in the afternoon to find a note saying she had gone in town to "attend to business matters." She would return weary and discouraged or elated and triumphant, over what I never understood, but have gathered since that when she was not conferring with Mr. Gilpatrick she was at the Boston Safe Deposit & Trust Company having long discussions with old Mr. Blodgett, her adviser, about trust funds, her will, and so on.

Of course she was concerned about our futures, especially mine. She used to sit me down and say to me earnestly:

"Amanda, I am arranging things so that when I am gone there will be enough money to take care of all of you. No one, not even you, can touch a penny of the money from this trial until you are twenty-one years old and if, when you reach the age of forty"—she always chose forty as the age for my breakdown—"you find that you are unable to cope with things, of course you will probably be perfectly well you understand, but *if* for some reason due to the shock of the accident, you are affected in your later life, you will always have this money I am fighting so hard to get. Then you will look back and be grateful to me."

I remember wishing after these sessions that I could feel the gratitude I ought to and wishing too that she would stop fighting so hard.

BATS

Just after Christmas that year at the Doughertys we were faced with what seemed at the time a tragedy. I arrived home from school one day to find the flat empty, Rachel and Phoebe off playing with friends, Mother on one of her expeditions into town, and Bridget in Brockton on her day off. A note was pinned to my pillow.

"My dear Lalapaloosa, please tell your dear mother that I feel so bad about doing it I couldn't tell her myself. I am leaving you all. I hate to go for you have been my family for six years now but I feel I must. Pretty soon, I hope next fall, wedding bells will be ringing for me!—and I want to be in Brockton to get ready. Please try to understand and forgive your Lala."

When Mother returned that afternoon and I had tremulously handed her the note she was shocked:

"Oh no! No! I can't *believe* Bridget would do such a thing. Why I've loved her! She's been like my own child! How could she—not even to tell me . . ." and she broke into tears, Phoebe and I noisily joining in.

"I think it was mean of her," said Rachel. "She *should* have told you."

"Yes, Rachel, she should have," said Mother blowing her nose and drying her eyes with her sodden handkerchief, "but she probably *couldn't*. We must remember that the poor child didn't *know* it was the wrong thing to do. You see, girls, *you* know because I've tried to bring you up to consider other people. And I can't hold it against

Bridget. She was a pillar of strength to me when I needed her the most!"

For weeks after that we were all depressed. Whenever I thought of Bridget I burst into tears and Mother said over and over, "Oh I miss her so. She was like my own child."

Not long after that we arrived home from school one day to find Mother neatly dressed in her blue serge suit, her hair prettily waved, her face glowing.

"Girls," she exclaimed almost as soon as we set foot in the door, "I think it's time we did something to perk ourselves up. How would you like to go on a bat this afternoon?"

"Yes," we cried.

Without more ado we changed into our best clothes and off we set for the streetcar on Beacon Street a few blocks away.

First we went for an early supper at the Dupont Restaurant near the Park Street subway. We always went to the Dupont or the DeLuxe or the Ambassador restaurants all run by the Ginter management.

"Now, girls, this is a special occasion," Mother said as we sat down, "so you may order whatever you like. I'm going to splurge myself this evening and have lobster salad."

During dinner she told us about the movie we were going to see, *The Young Rajah* with Rudolph Valentino.

"This is a fascinating story, girls, by Booth Tarkington, one of his best," and she proceeded to hand out morsels of the plot, just enough to sharpen our appetites. "This young Indian prince is able to foretell the future. And I particularly want you to notice the scene with the old man on the rocking horse. I hope they do it as well in the movie as in the book."

After dinner we walked down West Street to Washington and the Bijou Dream Theatre. We always went to the

Bijou Dream because it had an escalator and Mother did not have to climb stairs and get out of breath. Bordering the escalator was a flight of steps which we girls always used, very intriguing for they were made of glass and underneath them flowed a never ending stream of beautiful green water.

I was thrilled with what we were to see. For me Rudolph Valentino was the most romantic young man one could possibly imagine, and although Mother never admitted it beyond saying he was "an extraordinarily graceful dancer," I suspected she felt the same. Rachel preferred Ramon Navarro and Phoebe did not like any of the grown-up actors except Charlie Chaplin and Harold Lloyd, but she sat quietly through the entire movie except once to whisper to Mother, "Why is he spitting on her hand?" so loudly that the people around turned and stared at us.

After the moving picture came a long series of vaudeville acts. During one of them, a man with a white poodle who jumped through hoops and climbed steps, Mother leaned across me to whisper to Rachel "I don't approve of this sort of thing. Shall we leave?" whereupon I set up such a protest that we stayed where we were.

I never knew my mother to leave in the middle of any stage or screen performance, though she frequently threatened to do so, except once during a Marian Davies movie about the French Revolution, I believe, when Miss Davies, in her role as a peasant girl, runs after a coach load of lords and ladies, sticking out her tongue and bawling at the top of her lungs, "Down with the aristocrats! Down with the aristocrats!" to the cheers of the majority of the audience. Mother gathered us together and we left the theater —there was no gainsaying her that time—but I remember too, that in order not to disappoint us, she took us to another movie that same evening and in a theater with no escalator.

All during the evening Mother was in the best of spirits, laughing and talking, Rachel and Phoebe and I eagerly following along in whatever conversational direction her fancy took her. But on the way home, when we reached the Central Square Subway, she was seized with a fit of coughing.

"I'm sorry, girls, but I'll have to stop," she gasped.

So we stood against the wall of the subway, the jostling, careless crowd rushing past us, while Mother smoked her tin of Jones Powder. It was at least half an hour before she could attempt the steep flight of steps to the surface car, which took us along Beacon Street to our stop near the Cambridge-Somerville line.

As we grew older these expeditions grew more frequent. They were always the same: dinner at one of the Ginter restaurants and the moving pictures and vaudeville acts at the Bijou Dream Theatre. But the ends of those evenings were never as happy as their beginnings. It was always late and often on a school night and the memory of toiling home on the subway, standing for long periods at Central Square while Mother smoked her powder before mounting the stairs is not a happy one. People used to stop and stare at the quaintly dressed gray-haired woman gasping for breath and inhaling the evil smelling smoke from the burning can while we children squirmed miserably under their scrutiny. Occasionally a kind passerby would stop and ask if she could help and this would embarrass us even more.

When we finally reached home after the long frequently bitter cold walk from the streetcar, I used to wonder why Mother insisted on doing it so often.

AUNT BELLE

That winter, having held off as long as possible, Mother began reading us her favorite novel, *Pride and Prejudice.* "Girls, I think you're old enough now to appreciate Jane Austen's wit and good sense." And as she read, if we didn't react sufficiently, she would pause to expatiate on Mr. Bennet's dry humor or Mrs. Bennet's follies. The book reminded her of her own family and the jolly times they had together when they were young.

One evening as we were gathered around her rocking chair, happily absorbed in the chapter where Elizabeth Bennet goes to Netherfield to be with her sister, Jane, who is confined there with a bad cold, Mother paused in her reading: "This part always reminds me of my sister, Belle." she said.

I knew by the way she laid down the book that she was about to lapse into a long anecdote.

"Oh *please* don't stop reading," I said irritably.

"Why, Mother?" said Rachel. She was always more patient with Mother than I was.

Mother sat for a moment gazing into the distance as she always did when she was recalling her youth.

"Well—as you know—your Aunt Belle and I were very close—like the elder Bennet sisters. We used to have *such* happy times together . . ."

"Tell us about it," said I stretching myself full length on the carpet at her feet, resigned now to the inevitable.

"Oh, Belle was great company! She had a lovely clear

voice and she was always bringing home the latest songs. I used to play the piano for her. We made quite a team. People used to ask us to play and sing for them. And Belle was a wonderful sport, always ready to pick up and do *anything* anyone asked her. She was charming to *everyone*, too. She would dance, play charades, skate, coast, bicycle at the drop of a hat. She even learned to fence and to box, she and Hildred—Father insisted his daughters have the same advantages as his sons. I was never as athletic as they were."

"Tell about the time with the dolls," said Phoebe who had been having one of her late catnaps.

"No, tell about the cotton you used to drop," said I.

"One at a time, one at a time," said Mother laughing, "but do you really want to hear these stories all over again? Well, one Christmas, when Aunt Hildred and Aunt Belle and I were little girls, our parents gave us dolls for presents and we discovered them several weeks before Christmas Day hidden away in Mother's closet. We used to take them out and play with them when no one was watching and then wrap them up in their tissue paper and put them back in the closet. When Christmas morning came and the dolls were presented to us, Aunt Hildred and I pretended to be surprised but Aunt Belle who was only four or five, when she was given her doll, cried out, 'But that's *not* my dolly! That's Liza's!'"

"Now about the cotton," I said when we had stopped laughing.

"Let's see—we were about the same age, I guess—perhaps a little older—Aunt Belle and I were great companions, the way you and Phoebe are, Mandy. We used to take swabs of cotton on sticks, you know the kind, which we'd filched from Father's office, go upstairs to the bedroom we shared on the fourth floor. We'd dip the cotton into a big jar of vaseline, lean way out of the big front window—it's a marvel we didn't fall out—and drop them onto the people walking along Westminster Avenue. One afternoon we dropped one smack onto the top of a gentleman's tall silk hat. He was very angry indeed. It was a brand new hat. He came storming into the house to Father and Father had to pay for the hat. We never dropped any more cotton after that."

"Tell the story about the hat *you* bought," said Rachel. "I don't think the others have heard that."

"Oh, haven't they? Well, as I've often told you Aunt Belle was very witty, quick at repartee. Her timing was so good. That's what counts. One day I came home from a shopping spree. I used to love pretty clothes. I was really very extravagant, if you can believe it. Of course, Father was very lavish with us all. That day I had bought a hat and I'd paid twenty-five dollars for it! Imagine! That's what your father sends me for rent and food for us all. The hat was very elaborate and not in the best taste, I'm afraid. When I showed it to Belle she teased me about it. 'Liza,' she said and she said it with a completely straight face— she never laughed when she said something funny—that was the best part of it, 'I'd like to give you a piece of advice, if you don't mind. The next time you go shopping and you see something that you *know* you absolutely love, simply *must* have—avoid it!'" Mother chuckled. "Your father used to say that I laughed at everything Belle said whether it was funny or not. I guess I did. I loved her very much." Her eyes clouded and she averted her face from our gaze. "I miss her so terribly," she added and her voice sounded choked as if she were going to cry.

"She was awfully young to die, wasn't she?" Rachel offered.

"Just twenty-eight-years old."

"What did she look like?" I ventured in an effort toward happier topics.

"She looked like me, everyone said—only fair with deep blue eyes—sapphire blue they used to say."

"Was she pretty?" asked Phoebe.

"Not exactly pretty, but charming looking. Your Aunt Hildred was always considered the beauty of the family but I loved Belle's looks. Her face was so alive, and her figure was fairy-like—quick and graceful."

"Like you," said Rachel. "You're very quick and graceful."

"Thank you, dearie. And Belle was so gay and so vibrant—her face lighted up when she laughed and she was always laughing. It's hard to *believe* she's dead." Mother sat thinking for a moment. "I'll never forget that day as long as I live," she continued. "Grandpa telephoned and said Belle wanted to see me, that she wasn't well—he didn't mean physically ill, you understand—it was one of her depressions—and your Aunt Hildred drove me there in her horse and buggy—all the way from their farm in Dover she'd driven that morning to fetch me—your father was away from home at the time. When I got there Belle was in bed—not sick but very low in her mind. We talked for a long time—about lots of things—just before I left her she put her arms around me—I'll never forget," it was as if Mother were thinking out loud, as if we weren't there at all. "She put her arms around me and said so low I could just hear her words, 'Forgive me, Liza, forgive me.' The next day she was dead."

"Oh, how terrible!" cried Rachel. Phoebe put her arms around Mother's neck and sobbed with her.

"But, Mother," I said when she had regained her composure, "Why did she ask you to forgive her? What had she done?"

Mother sat thinking for a moment.

"Well, Mandy dear, it's a long story. As I've told you before, Aunt Belle was subject to terrible fits of depression

—melancholia it's called—she'd inherited it, according to Grandpa, from someone way back in the family—on my mother's side, he says, though *I'm* not convinced of *that*—and when she was in one of those deep depressions she was not herself—she said and did things that—weren't very considerate—that upset other people."

"What did she *say* to you?"

Mother sat gazing into the distance as if she hadn't heard me.

"It's not important any more," she said at last. "I forgave her long ago."

MAY PARTIES

The month of May was for me the loveliest month of the year. Every morning as I walked with my sisters to school the sweet smells from the newly budding trees and the small patches of garden along our way struck deep inside me, like a knife piercing my vitals. "Perced to the rote," seemed an excellent way to describe what I felt, but except for the first few lines of the Prologue, carefully paraphrased by Mother, all of us including Rachel were frankly bored with *The Canterbury Tales*. Sometimes Mother read us things whether we were bored or not. She seemed in a hurry to teach us everything she knew.

With May came Phoebe's birthday and May Parties. So

far as I can determine, this particular type of May party was peculiar to our locale and generation.

What I liked best about these parties was running them. Anything that required organization appealed to me: making up games, putting on impromptu skits, founding clubs (one club I founded at its first meeting elected me as president and Phoebe as ex-president). So I took charge of the guest list, selected the picnic spot and date, chose the king and queen, usually someone's little brother or sister (of course for our parties Phoebe was always queen), and assigned tasks to everyone, but when it came to the arduous work of making the wreaths and wands, fashioned from colored tissue paper with intricately crenulated rosettes, fluted edgings, and streamers to hang proudly down one's back or flutter in the breeze as one marched, my contributions were negligible. Since neither Mother nor Rachel seemed faintly interested in May Parties, Phoebe, who was superbly skillful at such handiwork, did it all.

The last party of the season that year was the one I gave with the help of my friend, Valerie Emerson. Everyone gathered on the appointed day dressed in her nicest party dress with her wreath, wand, and streamers and a bag of lunch, and after considerable argument as to who should march with whom, quelled at last under my strident direction, a line was formed in two's, the royal members of course at the head.

There was consternation in the ranks because Valerie and her little brother, Randolph, who was to be Phoebe's king, were late in arriving. Regina Murphy, whose nose was out of joint because I had chosen Valerie as co-hostess instead of herself, was grumbling: "Honest to God, Mandy, I wish't you hadn't of ast them. I'm mad on you, honest to God I am! Ma she don't like me to play with them niggers anyways."

But just then the Emersons, their dark faces glistening

with sweat, came up apologizing for their unavoidable tardiness. Their mother, who went out by the day to clean people's houses, hadn't found time to buy gold paper for Randolph's crown until that morning. So Regina was spared a stiff lecture on intolerance.

Randolph was hurried into place beside Phoebe at the head of the line. What a handsome couple! He with his dark curls, she with her blond ones, both of them in white, as was customary for the king and queen. Exchanging proud glances, Valerie and I swung into the rear pulling a small cart (always a property of any May Party) filled with our lunch: Cheese Tidbits, bottles of pop, Hoodsies (all purchased from the corner store with returned nickels from empty milk bottles), and the procession set off along the sidewalk chanting as we marched:

> *May Party, May Party, rah! rah! rah!*
> *Are we in it? Well I guess we are.*
> *Two, four, six, eight, who do we appreciate?*
> *Cambridge, Cambridge, rah! rah! rah!*
> *Wrig-gely, Wrig-gely Spearmint gum*
> *Who put Somerville on the bum?*
> *Cambridge, Cambridge, rah! rah! rah!*

The spectacle of other children, especially any of the Somerville Bums, off on their May Parties, had often filled Phoebe and me with the utmost scorn, they looked so absurd tramping along the sidewalks, with their thin dresses, fluttering streamers, and dusty old shoes, bawling ridiculous verses in hoarse voices, but our party seemed to us entirely natural and dignified.

Divinity Field was our destination, an original site for a picnic. I loved this oasis in the middle of Cambridge though it was a long distance, especially for the king and queen who had to take turns riding in the cart.

The morning was sultry, the trek was a weary one, the cart was heavy, our throats were sore from shouting and the verses were beginning to jar our ears, but we finally reached the field without more than the usual number of jeers from hoodlums along the way and were just sitting on the grass, a treat after the hot pavements, ready to take out our lunches, when I noticed a young man in horn-rimmed glasses a little distance away sitting on some winter board-walks which had been piled up for the summer. On closer scrutiny I saw that he was reading a book, that his trousers were opened, and his private parts plainly exposed.

It was not the first time my sisters and I had been confronted by an exhibitionist in Cambridge but this was particularly distressing in the atmosphere of our lovely May Party with so many little children present. After a whispered conference with Valerie and Regina, without telling the real reason to the younger ones (of course I told Phoebe later as I told her everything), we gathered up pop bottles, Cheese Tidbits, Hoodsies, and streamers and moved camp to another spot as far away as possible.

When we got home that afternoon I decided not to mention this episode to Mother; she might forbid us to go to Divinity Field again. But the truth was I never felt the same about it after that—or about May Parties either.

PART THREE

Vassal Lane

BOARDING HOUSES

IN JUNE, after a little more than a year of living at the Doughertys, Mother put most of our furniture, including our piano, in storage and we moved again, this time to a boarding house on Wendell Street. We girls hated leaving the Doughertys, but since Bridget's departure Mother was finding it increasingly difficult to do all the housework by herself. Her attacks of asthma were more frequent now and lasted longer.

Our new landlord, Mr. LaRue, had been a chef before he married, and Mrs. LaRue, Mother told us in low tones soon after we moved there, was "common." Mother felt sorry for Mr. LaRue because he did all the work in the house and looked "worn to a frazzle."

In the LaRue's sunroom there was a player piano and a phonograph and after dinner Mrs. LaRue used to sit with some of the men boarders and sing "improper" songs— "I'll hold you and fold you 'til dreams all come true but give me the moonlight, the June light and you," and a great many others which Mother, after the first few evenings, forbade us to listen to, much to Phoebe's and my own disappointment. This meant we had to go straight to our rooms after supper.

The LaRues had an eight-month-old baby. This enchanted Phoebe, who loved to "mind" babies, and at first she wheeled him out in his carriage every afternoon, but

Mrs. LaRue so seldom changed his diapers and he smelled so in consequence that Phoebe had to give it up.

We stayed at the LaRues' for only a few months. Mother decided that Mrs. LaRue's playing of the victrola all day and singing improper songs in the evening was a bad influence on us so she found another place to board with a family named Hanson in Vassal Lane. Vassal Lane was a small side street running from Huron Avenue to Fresh Pond, so distant from school that we all three had to take a streetcar. From every standpoint, life at Vassal Lane was the lowest point in our Cambridge existence.

Mrs. Hanson, a big, brawny, homely woman from Nova Scotia, sang no songs of any kind and did no flirting with the men boarders, but had I been consulted I would have chosen Mrs. LaRue any day. Mr. Hanson was Swedish and good looking in a flashy gold-toothed way, more attractive than his wife, but "cut from the same cloth," Mother said. Their small son, Wesley, (his mother insisted on pronouncing it "Wellesley") used to weep every morning because his parents wouldn't tie his shoe laces.

There were several boarders beside ourselves. The only one I remember was Mr. Duffy, an elderly Irishman with a huge stomach and a W. C. Fields nose and complexion who was always slightly intoxicated and who frequently appeared in the hall on his way to the bathroom we all shared, or at the breakfast table, in his yellow winter undershirt and suspenders. Everyone sat down to meals in the Hanson's narrow dining room so we knew a good deal about each other.

The menu every night, almost without exception, was corned beef and cabbage, a dish which Rachel and Phoebe and I detested, especially Phoebe. Rachel would eat the corned beef, I the cabbage, but Phoebe, who was fussy at best and only liked potatoes, discovered they had been stewed for hours with the cabbage and the corned beef. As a result she ate nothing.

We four would go upstairs to our rooms every night after dinner and huddle around the oil stove (Mrs. Hanson saved on coal too) while Mother made us Horlick's malted milk or beef tea, and we would fill up on these and Educator Biscuits.

But worst of all were our lunches. We had to take sandwiches to school every day because it was too far to come home and every day they were exactly the same, slabs of heavy bread sodden with grape juice and paraffin (Mrs. Hanson had put up a bountiful supply of grape jelly which had not jelled properly and the paraffin had melted into it.) Phoebe was particularly miserable; not only could she not eat them but she felt ashamed when her friends brought out their daintily wrapped, delectable sandwiches. She used to throw hers into the wastebasket under the teacher's desk so no one would see them.

We celebrated one Christmas with the Hansons at Vassal Lane. I remember Mother putting our Christmas tree in their backyard with suet on it for the birds, but that is the only pleasant memory I have of the place, and in the following September after more than a year of corned beef and cabbage, the streetcar, and grape juice sandwiches in our knapsacks we moved again. But I am getting ahead of my story.

MARTHA WRIGHT

It was not until we had moved to Vassal Lane and I was eleven years old in the sixth grade that I began to enjoy going to school. The fifth grade with Marietta MacDougall had been a particularly bad year. That winter Mother had seemed especially worried about me. She had always fussed about me since the accident but that year she fussed more than usual. I was not playing out of doors with the others; she thought I looked poorly and was constantly urging me to stay home from school.

"If you feel the least bit tired when you wake up, Amanda, just don't try to get up. Stay home and rest for the day. It won't make any difference."

After this advice there were many wintery mornings when I *didn't* feel like getting up and stayed in bed while the others trudged off. This was a great luxury until about ten o'clock when the novelty had worn off and boredom had set in. Then the first thing I knew I was behind in my work. This worried me terribly.

I have often wondered why Mother felt it necessary to urge me to stay home from school. I suppose the doctors had frightened her about me. Certainly I was a highly nervous child with a number of bad habits, chewing my fingernails, wetting the bed, and so on. My worst trait was a violent temper. My sister, Rachel, reminded me years later that, as quite a big girl, I once lay down in the subway and kicked and screamed because I couldn't have my own way about something. I remember suffering torments and sulking for hours at a time, one day especially, with my head buried in the laundry bag in the closet where I had retreated because I could not have the biggest Easter basket, the one plainly marked "Rachel" by my grandmother who had sent them. Occasionally there was some effort on Mother's part to discipline me, but the attitude generally was that I was "nervous" and "delicate."

I was not the only nervous one in the family. Phoebe was a bedwetter too and Rachel used to walk in her sleep and have terrible nightmares about God and death. I remember her when she was still little waking up and screaming and rushing to Mother's room to ask her why we were here on this earth. I cannot remember Mother's answer.

The sixth-grade year began badly, worse even than the fifth. During the very first week I had a run-in with Miss Lanahan about my clothes. The other girls wore cotton dresses to school but Mother sent us in jerseys and jersey bloomers, dark and serviceable and easy to launder. One morning Miss Lanahan said she would like to have a "little talk" with me and took me outside in the corridor. Anticipating trouble I waited uneasily, my eyes glued to the enormous yellow brooch pinned to the stuff of her dress, seemingly jabbed not merely through it and the pink corset beneath but clear through the tightly folded breasts as well. She cleared her throat nervously: "Now, Amanda, I'm very sorry to say this but I don't think it's quite *nice* for a little girl to come to school without a skirt over her bloomers. Do you?"

My embarrassment was so excruciating I could only hang my head and shift from one foot to the other. That afternoon when I went storming home to Mother she was furious.

"The woman doesn't have a scrap of taste" she said, but after that I wore skirts to school.

Then Martha Wright came into my life. Getting to know

her was one of the most significant happenings in my childhood; until then I had never had one particular pal. Of
course I never designated Martha as that even in my
thoughts. Solecisms like "pal," "chum," and "buddy" were
abhorrent to my mother, in a class with "fella" and "swell."
Nor could one say "vest" or "pants," but "waistcoat" and
"trousers"; a gentleman never "tipped" his hat, he "raised"
it. There were a host of others.

On this one subject my grandmother and my mother
were in perfect agreement. My grandmother's chief abomi-
nations were: "mailman" for "postman," "making" eggs
instead of "cooking" them—the hen made them—and
"home" when one meant "house."

The trouble was that most of the people at Agassiz used
every one of these prohibited words and a great many others besides. Martha Wright was my first friend who did
not.

She was a comely little girl with slanting blue eyes,
chestnut hair, and pink cheeks, with a shrewd almost sharp
expression in her eyes and mouth disturbing in one so
young, but to me fascinating. She wore her beautiful hair
in a low side part with a thick shining wing drooped over
one eye exactly like Colleen Moore. However intensely I
admired and envied this glamorous coiffure, no amount of
wetting and combing could accomplish the same for me.
Everything Martha had or did I tried to emulate. She
had bright red cheeks; I was pale, which I detested. In the
wintertime I used to walk to school pressing handfuls of
snow or ice to my cheeks until they burned, then run
quickly up to my classroom to arrive before my normal
pallor returned. Martha was shorter than I and slouched
badly with one hip jutting out in what I considered a stylishly alluring manner and I did my best to imitate her but I
never *felt* stylish. Besides it was uncomfortable.

Every teacher had a pet and it was plain from the very

first day of school that Martha was Miss Lanahan's. Until this time I had scorned pets but now I decided I *must* be one. This proved a hopeless ambition. I was as sweet as I could be—a radical change—and attended to my studies religiously, watching every paper that was handed back to me and to Martha in order to keep track of our grades but no matter how many E's (for excellent) were mine or how many VG's or G's were Martha's, at the end of each marking period the list on the blackboard was always headed "Martha Wright" never "Amanda Willard."

Penmanship was my real downfall. Martha was a master at the Palmer Method, her fine feathery scrolls obviously accomplished the correct way, "from the shoulder please," whereas mine were the worst in the class, cramped and ugly and spattered with blots, and sometimes in a fit of frustration scratched right through the paper in an ugly tear, the unforgivable offense in Miss Lanahan's eyes. So although I might sometimes be third on the blackboard list or even second I was *never* first. It was only when I reached the eighth grade with Susie Simpson that I became a pet at last but it didn't matter any more. Martha had moved away.

Martha was the second of four children: an older sister, a younger sister and a boy, Sonny, only five when I first knew him. A handsome little fellow with large black eyes, dark skin, and curly black hair, he was a striking contrast to his fair-skinned sisters. I used vaguely to wonder about him sometimes but it wasn't until years later, long after I had left Cambridge, that the mystery of the Wright family suddenly revealed itself to me.

Toward the end of the year Martha finally asked me home one afternoon after school. Although we had become the best of friends and I had repeatedly asked her to our rooms at the Hanson's, she had never accepted and had never returned the compliment. This worried me. When I went I realized why. Martha's father and mother were divorced, a most unusual circumstance in the 1920's. The children lived with their father and Martha and her older sister did all the housework.

The instant we arrived we set to work making beds, doing dishes, washing and ironing clothes, scrubbing the kitchen floor. I was much impressed by their independence in setting to work with no one to cajole or flatter them into it as Mother did with us—"Amanda, dear, those are the finest pancake eggs I've ever tasted."

The older sister who bore the brunt of the responsibility was not as pretty as Martha; her life had made her expression angry, her voice sharp. When I first arrived that afternoon her manner to me was sarcastic, almost rude, but as soon as she realized she needn't be ashamed of the shabby place in front of me she relaxed and soon we were all three roaring with laughter at everything—our teachers, our classmates, ourselves.

One afternoon a few weeks after this, when Martha and I were walking past the grounds surrounding the public library, we saw sitting on one of the public benches, a big wicker baby carriage nearby, a large woman, heavily made up, her hair bleached brassy blond, her untidy dress half unbuttoned displaying an abundant expanse of white bosom. To my surprise the woman called out a breezy greeting to Martha:

"Well for god sakes look who's here! How are ya, Queenie?"

"Fine," Martha replied. The woman glanced at me but Martha made no move to introduce us.

"That's swell, honey. On ya way home from ticklin' the books?" and she laughed loudly.

Martha nodded and smiled her bitter smile and was about to move on but the woman stretched out a hand and laid it on her arm.

"Gee, kid, I was awful sorry about the other night, but I di'n know who else ta call. You're not mad at me are ya?" She smiled affectionately at Martha and her smile was surprisingly sweet. "Honest to God I was neary sick worryin' over this"—she indicated the baby carriage—"hope it di'n bother ya too much." Then without pausing for Martha's answer, "If ya knew how sick and tired I get follerin' them doctors all over the joint. Honest to God!" and she pulled a package of cigarettes from the shiny leather handbag on the bench near her. I was taken aback. I had never seen a woman smoke before. "Gee you kids are somethin'!" she went on, then turning to me she added, "She and her big sister knows more about babies than I do," and she laughed again. "Take a peep why doncha?" pulling back the mosquito netting draping the carriage, "The little devil ain't asleep, don't worry," and she inhaled deeply on her cigarette while I watched fascinated.

Martha bent to the carriage. I was just behind peering over her shoulder.

"He's awful cute," I murmured. The baby was black. After a few more exchanges Martha and I went on our way.

"Bye, kid" the woman called after us, "Bring yer friend around sometime, why doncha," she added pleasantly. Martha and I walked on in silence.

"Who was that?" I was unable to restrain my curiosity any longer.

"My mother," Martha said.

One afternoon a few weeks after this episode Martha came at last to our rooms at the Hanson's to meet Mother.

"What a nice little girl," Mother said after she had gone. "Have you met her mother?"

"Her mother's dead" I said. It seemed wiser not to explain.

Martha and I were devoted friends for two years and

then in the fall of our eighth-grade year the Wrights moved from Cambridge to Woburn to a real house all to themselves with a big yard around it. This was nice for them but a terrible blow to me. There was no one to take Martha's place. None of the other girls in my class were anything like her.

I was determined, however, that the move would make no difference, that we would go on being as good friends as ever, and three times that fall I rode all the way on my bicycle, miles down Massachusetts Avenue through Arlington and Winchester to Woburn, vowing all the while that things would be just the same. But gradually I had to give up. Martha was too busy to come to see me; in any case she had no bicycle and the streetcar trip was interminable. The thought crossed my mind more than once that she wasn't making as much of an effort as I was. After my third trip I had to face the fact that it never *could* be the same. She and her sister had new friends, new teachers. There was nothing to laugh about any more.

I saw Martha once years later when I was in college. I had gone into an ice cream place on Massachusetts Avenue near my dormitory. There in a soiled white uniform serving ice cream over the counter was my friend. She had the same beautiful hair, the same slanting eyes and pink cheeks, but the smile was gone and she seemed only faintly glad to see me.

UNCLE JAMES

That winter when we lived at Vassal Lane, Bessie telephoned, as she had before, to invite us to Grandpa's, this time for Christmas dinner, and as always before Mother declined. Her excuse was the same, that it was too much for Grandpa, now that he was old and feeble, to have so many children around. But we had seen Grandpa only a few days before when he came to the Hanson's to call on us, as lively and garrulous as ever. Now that we were older we were less amenable than when we were little and all of us protested, I most vociferously, but no amount of arguing did any good. Mother was adamant.

At last, thoroughly frustrated and angry, I went into one of my prolonged sulks, this one lasting two long wretched days, at the end of which everyone including myself was worn out. On the second afternoon, to dispel my nasty mood, mother suggested her remedy for almost everything, a bat.

"I don't want to go on any old bat," I said rudely.

"Come, Mandy dear," Mother urged. "Don't spoil your own and everyone's happiness."

"Then why do you spoil my happiness?" I growled.

Mother shook her head and turned away. The hurt look in her eyes troubled me. I yearned to throw my arms around her and tell her how sorry I was I had been so hateful and please to forgive me; secretly too I was longing to go. The moving picture was Rudolph Valentino in *The Son of the Sheik,* but some force deep inside me, black and bitter, had me in its grip and I could do nothing.

I lay on my cot in the dark little bedroom, my mouth muffled by the pillow, my eyes swollen with weeping, listening to Mother in the next room speaking in a low voice to Rachel and Phoebe. Although she had implied earlier that *they* were going anyway and that if I chose to stay at home I would only be "biting off my nose to spite my face," she was saying now that she couldn't leave me alone and that we would have to go another time. Rachel argued mildly for a few minutes and Phoebe fussed and said she thought it was "mean," then after a bit they gave in and went out to see if they could find some coal or ice pungs to hop, there being very little else to do, leaving Mother and me alone, Mother rocking and coughing, I in the next room sodden with self-pity.

At last I could bear it no longer. Rousing myself I tottered to the door and stood in silence in the semidarkness gazing at my mother's profile outlined in the narrow window against the white darkness of the winter twilight. She turned when she saw me.

"Come here, Mandy," she whispered, holding out her arms while I flung myself on her breast. "Oh my poor Mandy, I worry about you, my dearest, I worry about you," and we wept together.

"I want to go on the bat! I want to go on the bat!" I wailed.

"It's too late, dearie," she said gently. "We'll go another day very soon."

Fortunately I was too worn out to insist. We sat together, I on the floor at her feet, gazing out of the window at the dreary winter evening, at the soot blackened piles of snow on Vassal Lane, in the distance over the jagged line of the rooftops the nacreous sky.

"Why don't you ever go to Grandpa's?" My tone was gentle, respectful. "Is it really because of Aunt Belle's death?"

For a moment she didn't answer, just looked at me in that quizzical way of hers.

"Amanda, there are some things—though heaven knows I tell you and Rachel *almost* everything—that are difficult for a child to understand."

"I think I can understand," I said. "Please tell me."

She sat for a long moment in the pose so familiar to me, one foot tucked under her, her arm resting on the arm of the mahogany chair, her gray-blue eyes gazing at me speculatively.

"Perhaps I should, Mandy. Perhaps you *are* old enough now to know some of these things. God knows I've tried to bring you girls up without *all* the burdens of the generation ahead of you—but, as the Bible says, 'the sins of the fathers are visited upon the children, yea even unto the third and the fourth generation'—and you, my poor little girls, are suffering for just *that*—the sins of your father."

"You mean—it's because of *Father* that you don't go to Grandpa's!"

"Yes—partly because of him—and because of Uncle James."

"Uncle James?" I had suspected all along that he had something to do with it.

"Yes, Amanda. The reason I never go to Westminster Avenue is because of your Uncle James. The last time I was there he *ordered* me to *leave* the house! My *father's* house, *not* his, my *home* where I had been brought up!"

"But that's terrible!" I was indignant. "*Why* did he do such a thing?"

"He ordered me out of my father's house because he was very angry with me." She spoke each word slowly, dramatically. "And when I left that house that day I made a vow that I would *never* cross the threshold again—and I never have!" Then all at once, my mother's voice was mournful. "My poor old father has had to suffer as a result

—I'm sick at heart at the thought of the poor old man having to suffer this way in his old age—but he wouldn't take a stand at the time—he allowed James to send me away—right before his eyes—he let me go and never called me back—until afterwards when it was too late—the damage had been done."

"But what happened? Why did Uncle James order you out of the house? And what had Father to do with it?"

"It's such a long story, Mandy, I can't tell it all now—some day I will but not now. You know about your father. I've told you some of it and you've heard Grandpa and me talking—about his behavior with other women—from the early days of our marriage—his treachery—"

"Yes, I know."

"Well, and you know—I've told you—how I tried more than once to separate from him and how each time he insisted that I take him back and I did—but then when he had gone so far, had committed the final outrage—had behaved so terribly—my whole family told me I *must* leave him—Uncle James in particular came over to see me more than once—talked with me earnestly trying to get me to make up my mind to leave him—and I did leave him for good *this* time, I thought, but your father came to me and begged me, literally *begged* me, on his knees, to take him back," she sighed deeply. "And so I took him back—he could be very persuasive—and I felt so sorry for him. I went in to a doctor on Commonwealth Avenue in Boston, a specialist in these matters whom your grandfather had recommended to me. I consulted him as to what I should do—Oh, Mandy, you'll never know what I went through—and he said to me, 'Mrs. Willard, this man you're married to will never be any different. You must make up your mind that you cannot change him but I do not know how to advise you. You can't live with him and you can't live without him.' So I took him back—against the wishes of my whole family. And when I went there to Grandpa's house your Uncle James was furiously angry with me—James has a frightful temper—he shouted at me—I had gone over there to comfort Father—it was after Aunt Belle's death and he had *asked* me to come—and James stormed at me and said dreadful things about your father, and when I tried to defend him, tried to say he was weak and that we should be forgiving, he grew angrier than ever. 'You are a fool, Eliza Willard, and you are living with a monster,' he said and then he ordered me out of the house. 'Get out,' he said, 'and never come back!' and I never have. It broke up our whole family. None of them has ever forgiven me for taking your father back. My brother, Freddy, moved away from Boston soon afterward, I'm sure that was one reason he went, and even your Aunt Hildred has behaved coolly toward me and toward Grandpa too."

"But why toward Grandpa?"

"Because Grandpa forgave your father, too. He *used* to like Archie and he wanted to help him—he said we *must* forgive him but no one, not even Grandpa, can *really* forgive him. Grandpa came and stayed with us in Brookline for a while to make it up to me and to try to help Archie—but it didn't do any good."

"And you left Father after that?"

"Yes, I left him at last. I had to. But not until a year later, after he had gone straight back to his old wretched life. Then I knew I couldn't go on. Uncle James was right of course and I wrote and told him I was leaving Archie but he never answered my letter. And I asked him once to come to see me when I was having one of my worst attacks of asthma. He wouldn't come. I've never asked him again. He and I have never spoken since. He has refused to have anything to do with me—my *brother* who helped to bring me up—Mother died when I was so young, you know. . . .

Oh Mandy, don't ever, *ever* have any bitterness between you and your sisters, no matter *what* they or you may do. Bitterness between brothers and sisters can be a terrible thing."

I promised solemnly that I never would and just then Rachel and Phoebe returned from their pung hopping, fresh and red-cheeked, and Mother jumped to her feet saying: "Girls, what do you think? It's a Friday night and you can sleep tomorrow—shall we go on our bat after all?"

VICE

Although Mother talked a lot about God, urging us to have faith in Him and so on, I had the impression that she had been badly disappointed in Him. Her favorite quotation from the Bible was: "Unto everyone that hath shall be given . . . but from him that hath not shall be taken away even that which he hath."

She talked a lot too about vice. She had her own version of Oscar Wilde's *The Picture of Dorian Gray*, a nightmarish tale of a beautiful young man whose face remained young and innocent while the face in his portrait gradually deteriorated, reflecting the disintegration of his soul. I think Wilde's story reminded her of Father because she often said: "Your father used to be a very beautiful young man," and "One thing I can say for Archibald Willard. He gave me my three beautiful children."

I always liked it when she said these things and always secretly hoped, for her sake more than for mine, that perhaps some day they would be reunited.

We had not seen Father for over two years, not since his visit to us at 8 Wellington Street, and I suspected, though she never said so, that this was as much Mother's doing as his. Perhaps she was ashamed of Vassal Lane or perhaps she may not have wanted him to see her looking like a "haggard old witch," and although we assured her that this was not so, when on occasion I studied her face, I had to admit to myself that she *was* old.

For Mother's sake I was sorry that Father never came any more, for though "wild horses wouldn't have dragged it" from her, I had the feeling that she still cherished the memory of their romance. The spring after we had moved to Vassal Lane, however, we arrived home from school one afternoon to find the beds still unmade, the rooms still untidy, and Mother pacing the floor. A letter had come from Father demanding a divorce.

The possibility of divorce had been suggested in the past by both Father and Grandmother Willard in a desultory way but Mother had never taken it very seriously and had always categorically refused, ostensibly because he would not support us adequately. But this time he was emphatic: "If you refuse to start proceedings for divorce in this country," he wrote "I shall go to Paris and obtain one myself."

"Oh, it's very plain what has happened," Mother said when she had finished reading us the letter. "He has some woman now who insists on marriage. But never! I'll never give him a divorce!"

"But, Mother," said Rachel hesitantly, "wouldn't it be better that way?"

"Don't you see, Rachel," and Mother's eyes glittered, "if I did that I'd be playing straight into their hands. That's just what he wants, to be free of us all! Free of his responsibilities! Free to marry again or do any damnable thing he wishes! And his mother, that faithless woman, is backing him to the hilt! Little does she care that her grandchildren are living in squalor! Do you know that she wrote and asked why, now that the settlement has been made on the accident, I didn't buy a house somewhere? She expects me to take the money I've fought so hard for and spend it on our support. But I'll *never* do it! That money has been put in trust for you children when I am gone. It's your father's duty to support his family."

All that afternoon the talk went on. After our dinner of corned beef and cabbage in the Hanson's dining room, as soon as we set foot in our upstairs rooms it began again. I had never seen my mother so upset. Although none of us dared to repeat Rachel's question of the afternoon, Mother must have divined our thoughts or perhaps she was arguing with herself.

"No! I'll never give him a divorce. Do you think he'll care one rap what happens to us if he's free? If some woman gets her clutches on him? No! He'll never—mark my words—he'll *never* marry again until I am dead!"

We had been sitting around our oil stove (although it was springtime the room was cold), Mother talking and talking, Rachel and I struggling to keep awake. It was very late. We had long since finished munching our Educator Biscuits and sipping our beef tea, when Phoebe who had fallen asleep as usual on Mother's bed, suddenly sat up.

"Why does Father do such wicked things?" she said.

For a long moment Mother did not answer, but sat thinking, her head in her hand, her eyes studying the worn carpet under her rocking chair.

"It's hard to explain, Phoebe," she said at last. "There is always evil in the world, just as there is good. And some people are more tempted by it than others. They don't have the strength to resist, I guess . . . and the more they yield to

temptation the less wicked their behavior seems to them.
You remember—I've recited it to you before—what Alexander Pope said about vice?" She looked at each of us
in turn, then slowly, dramatically she rang out the lines. I
can still feel the horror that swept over me as I listened to
the words, still envision my father struggling desperately in
the clutches of that hideous monster.

> *Vice is a monster of so frightful mien*
> *As to be hated needs but to be seen;*
> *Yet seen too oft, familiar with her face,*
> *We first endure, then pity, then embrace.*

NANTASKET BEACH

Father's threats and demands were of no avail; he had no
grounds for divorce in this country or anywhere else. But
Mother was disturbed for a long time after the letter.
Whenever his name was mentioned she was more bitter
than ever before. Soon after she came down with her worst
attack of asthma, which lasted for weeks, well into the
summer.

Late in July, after Rachel had gone to Maine, Phoebe
and I woke up one hot morning to find Mother sitting in
her rocking chair breathing hard and looking very drawn.
The night before she had promised us that if the weather
was fine and she was feeling better she would take us to
Nantasket Beach.

In the early days when we were little, after Father had gone and there was no one to drive us, Mother and Grandpa used to take us all to Nantasket Beach on the steamer. Neither Mother nor Grandpa ever entered the water, although I do have a faint, early recollection of Mother in a green silk bathing costume with long black stockings. Since then she had had to give it up because cold water made her asthma worse. So she and Grandpa would sit smiling on the beach, Mother in her long-skirted old-fashioned suit with the accordian skirt, because it was chilly on the steamer, and her black straw hat with the roses, under a black umbrella, and Grandpa in tan linen and a panama, while we three thrashed happily about on our water wings.

We almost always went to Nantasket, the Coney Island of Boston's South Shore, because we could get there and back by boat. We girls got to know the way intimately: first a surface car to Harvard Square, then the subway to Park Street, then to the upper southbound level and another surface car marked "Rowes Wharf." This let us off near the Nantasket Steamship Line where we took a steamer to the beach, a trip of about an hour.

When we grew older and Mother and Grandpa grew less able to go on these jaunts, Mother allowed Rachel (who was now her right hand) to take Phoebe and me, until the time came when Rachel went off to Maine for most of the summer.

Above all other things Phoebe and I loved to go swimming, so it was with a good deal of excitement that we had been anticipating this particular day.

"I'm so sorry, girls," Mother gasped as soon as she could get her breath, "I know you're going to be so disappointed but I just can't go anywhere today. I'm too ill . . ." and she had to stop for a fit of coughing. "Perhaps next week I can do it," she went on feebly but Phoebe and I were pretty

sure that next week would be just the same. We knew also
that there was no use asking her to let us go by ourselves;
we had tried many times before and she had always firmly
refused.

"Can I get you something?" said I halfheartedly.

"No, thank you," she answered smiling at me, but I was
too disappointed even to look at her and was about to
creep out of the room when she stopped me. "Amanda,
I've been thinking. Come here for a minute. You too,
Phoebe." We moved obediently to her side. "Do you think,
girls, that you might, if I tell you just how to go, be
able to ..."

"Yes! Yes!" we shouted in unison. Mother smiled at our
excitement. ". . . take the trip to Nantasket by yourselves?"

"Of course we can!" I cried echoed by Phoebe's "Of
course we can!" Then a twinge of conscience nudged me.
"But we don't want to leave you here all alone—when
you're so sick."

"No, we won't leave you," said Phoebe putting her arms
around Mother's neck and kissing her. Mother held on to
the little arm tightly and for one dreadful moment I
thought she was going to accept.

"Thank you—both of you girls for thinking of your sick
old mother—that's the way I want you to be, kind and
thoughtful of others, but I'll be fine here. Mrs. Hanson's
downstairs if I need anything and as a matter of fact it will
be a rest for me to be by myself for a while and to know you
two are having a good day by the seashore. Come home
and tell me all about it and it will be just as if I'd been
there."

This was something Mother was always saying that I
could never credit, that we could *tell* her about the pleasant things we'd been doing and that she would enjoy them
as much as if she'd been there herself.

"But you must *promise* me," she resumed in a firm tone, "not to speak to *anyone*—Amanda, you must see to it—not to *anyone*, man, woman, or child. Do you understand?"

We understood. After giving our solemn promise that we would speak to no one, wait an hour after lunch before swimming again, be careful not to lose our money, and take the four o'clock boat so we'd be home before dark, we dashed to our room to don our beach costumes: middy blouses, cotton bloomers, scarlet sweaters wound around our waists (until we got on the boat where it was cool) and knapsacks over our shoulders containing our bathing suits, bathing caps, and the dollar Mother gave each of us for the streetcar fare, boat fare, a bath house, and lunch. Then off we set with high hearts as if on an adventure to distant lands.

Almost immediately upon boarding the steamer it became obvious what our purpose there should be. There was a lot of "loose behavior" going on around us of which Mother would never have approved, although it wouldn't do to tell her about it of course for she might have put her foot down about our going again. We took it upon ourselves to correct this behavior. Accordingly we divided the ship in half, Phoebe to patrol the port side, myself the starboard. After a preliminary inspection, if we observed loose behavior: people holding hands, gazing into each other's eyes, standing with their arms around each other, or anything at all out of order, we were to report to headquarters immediately, join forces and remedy the situation by standing and staring sternly at the offending pair until they became ashamed of themselves. This we did conscientiously but with little success. Our task was especially taxing on the return trip, for we found that people were looser as the evening approached.

On the beach too we had considerable patrol duty. That

very afternoon when a couple were behaving outrageously right next to us I went to the water's edge, gathered up a bathing cap full of cold salt water and walking swiftly by threw it on the feet of the lovers. The man jumped up and chased me a good distance down the beach yelling obscenities, which scared me enough to curtail any future activities. I still felt, however, that it had been a duty well worth performing and Phoebe agreed with me absolutely.

We were scrupulous about carrying out Mother's instructions to the letter except in one respect. She had allotted twenty-five cents apiece, a considerable sum in those days, for the use of a bathhouse, but it seemed a pity to Phoebe and me to waste good money on *that*, so we wandered far up the beach away from the crowds and the hot dog stands to a scattering of small cottages, set on wooden piles driven into the sand, their underpinnings screened by crisscrossed wooden slats. Having selected a deserted-looking cottage and making sure no one was watching us, we crawled through the slats and in a prone position in the sand underneath the cottage we wriggled out of our middy blouses, bloomers and underthings into our bathing suits. Then returning to the crowds we had a lovely long swim followed by a lunch of hot dogs with mustard and piccalilli, and orange pop, and in the early afternoon, after another session under the cottage, we were in our dry clothes and ready for Paragon Park.

We had thoroughly explored every part of Paragon Park on previous trips with our elders so we knew that by far the best thing for our money was Hilarity Hall, which cost exactly the twenty-five cents we had saved by not using the bath house. This included all the most exciting attractions except the roller coaster, which Mother would not allow us to ride on anyway. Here were the Golden Twisters, funny mirrors, the Cakewalk, the Lemon Squeezer, and best of all the slides, three of them, a minia-

ture one for babies or sissies, a middle-sized one and another very long steep one with a high ladder (to mount
which required outstanding courage) and a wooden bowl
at the foot.

Nothing gratified Phoebe or me more than, clad in our
jaunty costumes, our sweaters around our waists, our
knapsacks slung over our shoulders military style, to fly
from one to another of these delights and nothing marred
the perfection of this or any other Nantasket day except
perhaps a painful sunburn. Even that had its pleasant side,
to arrive home and have Mother exclaim: "My goodness,
girls, what a beautiful color you are!"

PART FOUR

Sacramento Street

LIFE AT THE FLANNAGANS

THAT FALL we moved again, this time to Sacramento Street, where we were to spend almost a year and a half, the longest we had ever lived in one place. From 113 Sacramento Street it was a few blocks down Oxford Street to the Agassiz School; Rachel and Phoebe and I could easily walk there and come home for lunch, a great relief after Mrs. Hanson's grape and paraffin sandwiches.

We never knew the Flannagans as well as we had the Dougherty family. Mr. Flannagan was an undertaker and conducted his business in the front parlor of his house. His sign—JAMES H. FLANNAGAN FUNERAL PARLOR—stood on a post on the front lawn. Of course none of us children, not even the Flannagans' three daughters, Mary, Eileen, and Doris (pronounced "Dorus") were allowed to cross the threshold of the front parlor.

Mother must have been "pretty strapped," as she said, to move to these quarters. Now we were all four living in one small room with a tiny kitchenette adjoining (according to Mother a necessity after the corned beef and cabbage of the winter before).

In the room were two brass beds, two bureaus, Mother's rocking chair, a chair for Grandpa Evans when he came to call, a trunk covered with a scrap of oriental rug which served both as chair and table, Mother's old Singer sewing machine, an old fashioned commode with a basin and pitcher and a tiny curtained-off closet.

131

The room was on the second floor, down a long corridor from the bathroom which we shared with the other roomers and the Flannagan family on Saturday nights, there being no tub in their part of the house. The tub always had a thick ring around it on Saturday nights and we were never allowed to use it; Mother herself drew the line at using it at all and confined her ablutions to the commode in the corner where she took her sponge bath when we were out of the way. Mother was a very modest person.

Soon after we moved to Sacramento Street Mother announced one evening with great excitement that she had decided to have us all four eat our dinners next door at Mrs. Larkin's dining room. (Mrs. Flannagan did not serve meals to her lodgers.)

"Girls," said Mother, her eyes shining with pleasure, "I have given this a good deal of thought and I have decided to take some of my principal—heaven knows there's little enough of it—money that was left me by my mother when she died and which I swore I'd never touch—but I think it's important for us all, especially you growing girls, to have one nourishing meal a day—but more important than that, it will be good for your manners, table and otherwise, to associate with the kind of people we will meet at Mrs. Larkin's."

I could see nothing attractive about the people at Mrs. Larkin's. They were all old and not at all good looking, but Mother must have liked them for, although we four sat by ourselves at a small table, she frequently entered the conversation at the big table, her eyes lighting up, her face flushing with pleasure. Mother loved good conversation. To see her so sprightly was a joy to Rachel and Phoebe and me.

Everything went smoothly at Mrs. Larkin's until one evening Mother entered into a discussion with a Miss MacIntyre, who was getting her master's degree in History at Radcliffe, on the subject of Miss MacIntyre's thesis. The latter made the statement that the people in the dining room would be classified (for what reason they had to be classified I've forgotten) as the "upper strata of the bourgeoisie." Mother held her tongue but we all three knew instantly that she was angry with Miss MacIntyre and when we returned to the Flannagans' and the privacy of our room, she exploded:

"Just imagine that woman putting my family in the same category as the people in that dining room," she sputtered and that evening and into the night she fumed and fretted, muttering under her breath when not out loud, "I could tell that young woman a few things that might surprise her if I cared to. What does *she* know about *my* family!"

All of this surprised me for I had always thought of Mother as democratic. After that, although we continued to eat at Mrs. Larkin's, there was less conversation with the other table.

MORALS

Grandpa Evans, now over eighty and frequently incapacitated by asthma in spite of "the deep breaths," almost never came any more to see us and Mother had no chance of adult company except at Mrs. Larkin's dinners, occasional trips to town to consult her lawyer, and to Mr. Blodgett at the Boston Safe Deposit & Trust Company *and* Cousin Emma.

This relative, a second cousin once removed to Grandpa Evans, elderly and impoverished, had always admired my mother for her "spunk" and took it upon herself, since we were in such straitened circumstances, to come frequently to call with the kindly purpose of "bucking up Lizby," as she always called Mother. Unfortunately the admiration was not mutual; Mother found her dull and exasperating and told us more than once that she preferred solitude to Cousin Emma's company.

Cousin Emma, who had never married, had eccentric notions about life in general and marriage and men in particular. According to her, all men were "rotters" and the sooner dispensed with the better. Unlike Mother's own family, Cousin Emma had had little or no education. (Mother told how Cousin Emma's mother used to boast "I knowed all there was to be knowed about English grammar when I was twelve years old"), and her views were accordingly limited. It outraged Mother that Cousin Emma should reduce family principles to absurdities.

One afternoon her patience was tried more than usual. The subject of men and morals came up, as it always did when Cousin Emma came to call, and Cousin Emma made the statement that it was wrong, in fact wicked, to be married at all, that sex was a vile pursuit.

"You don't know what you're talking about, Emma," Mother said crossly, and "The woman's not balanced" to Rachel and Phoebe and me after Cousin Emma had left.

When she felt we had reached a suitable age Mother gave each of us a book, *The Three Gifts of Life*, which to Phoebe and me was not only incomprehensible but boring. That was the extent of our sex education. Mother never did tell us the facts of life. She had been brought up with strait-laced ideas which she passed on to us.

"Never allow a young man to put his arm around you or even hold your hand until you are engaged to be married. You may *shake* hands," but that was all.

One should never get oneself up in a "common way." "Avoid the very appearance of evil," and of course powder and rouge were only for street walkers; no lady would think of wearing make-up, except perhaps a touch of eyebrow pencil "to give character to the face," as in my own case where my eyebrow had been scarred.

We were warned about the fearful things that might ensue if we even *thought* bad thoughts and, like other children of that generation, were told in muted tones about the evils of masturbation, though I for one hadn't the slightest inclination, consciously at any rate, to do anything of the kind. It was odd that we knew such a lot about syphilis, gonorrhea, masturbation, illegitimacy, and loose behavior and still had no idea how babies came into existence.

On the subject of morals, my older sister, Rachel, was more of a concern than we younger ones. Unlike Phoebe and me, Rachel was not one to occupy the center of the stage and always sat back when we were telling stories or performing vaudeville acts, but she was a highly precocious and talented girl. Now at the age of thirteen she was fast developing a Clara Bow figure and this, with her pretty face, brilliant coloring, and long dark curls tied back with a velvet bow, was more than enough for boys to start noticing her. Mother, who had a keen eye for such things, began to worry.

Day after day through that winter a group of ardent youths followed Rachel home from school, all the way up Sacramento Street almost to our door. Mother issued stern injunctions as to how she must handle this.

"Don't speak a *single* word to them, Rachel, or even turn your head and you will find they will soon give it up," said Mother one morning before Rachel set off.

"But I *don't* speak to them, Mother. Really I don't and yet they keep on. They just won't leave me *alone*," replied Rachel almost in tears. I could tell from the way Mother's eyes narrowed that she wasn't convinced.

That afternoon, on my way home from school, I caught sight of Rachel a few yards ahead of me, her nose in the air, her dark curls under the green velveteen tam-o'shanter tossed by the wind, a determined set to her jaw, marching swiftly along the street with at least six boys bedeviling her with every kind of taunt and entreaty. Stepping unnoticed into the entrance to a grocery store nearby I watched the procession until one particularly bold and handsome youth bawled out: "Come on, kid, give us a kiss, woncha!"

I couldn't tolerate this. Springing onto the sidewalk I shouted after them angrily: "You leave my sister *alone*, d'ya hear!" whereupon they turned in a body to stare at the fierce little girl and for a moment were too surprised to speak.

"My mother's going to call the police if you don't stop!" I went on amazed at my ingenuity, and though their response was a loud guffaw it must have had some effect, for as Rachel disappeared around the corner of Sacramento Street, they slackened their pace, gave up the chase, and vanished.

Of course I reported the proceedings in detail to Mother that evening. After this the subject was dropped. I think Mother was finally reassured that Rachel was not "on the road to destruction."

THE TWENTY-FIFTH REUNION

In June of 1926 Mother was to celebrate her twenty-fifth Radcliffe reunion. Her classmate, Amelia Everett Whitman, the mother of Rachel's friends, was to have a garden party at her house on Divinity Place and everyone in the class of 1901 with their families was invited. Mother was looking forward to this with the greatest interest and excitement I had ever known her to display about anything of the kind; indeed it was the only social function she ever attended while I knew her.

Every detail of our wardrobe was planned to the last glove and sock weeks in advance. She went so far as to purchase a new blue lace dress for the occasion, the only dress I ever knew her to buy, taking Rachel with her in town to R. H. Stearns to help her make the selection. For us she spent many hours at her sewing machine making new white frocks, then another trip in town to buy us new black patent leather slippers.

For weeks she never stopped talking about it; it would be *such* an occasion, how proud she would be when we three entered that garden scene, jumping up to show us how we must walk, smile, shake hands, pleasant and gracious but reserved—not *too* effusive and eager—*that* would be poor manners. She hadn't seen any of her friends for many years.

"How amazed they'll be to see me with my three charming daughters. I'm going to be *so* proud of you girls. You've no idea!"

I remember feeling that this event was somehow going to alter the entire course of our lives; we were going to be discovered by some one of Mother's rich, influential classmates and everything was going to be different. I remember all of these preparations but the only recollection I have of the occasion itself is my mother smiling and shy, standing in a corner of the Whitmans' garden for the space of half an hour after which she made her adieux and with us in tow departed.

A VISIT TO WYCHMERE

After the reunion the atmosphere in our household was one of total anticlimax, as if there were nothing left to look forward to. The eagerness and interest that had sustained Mother through all her preparations in May and June had vanished. By July she was "down and out" with another of her now frequent attacks of asthma.

Our being in the city all summer was fretting her more than usual; my grandmother hadn't invited Rachel until August this year, and she worried constantly about money, saying that if Father didn't send us something pretty soon we'd be "out on the street," "on our way to the poorhouse," and so on, so frequently that it no longer made any impression on us. Money *must* have been very short, so short that we were unable even to go to Nantasket. The boat fare for three girls was expensive. Although we endeavored not to show it, we were fearfully restless confined to the one hot little room.

One stifling morning after a particularly wakeful night, the room never having cooled off at all, Mother called us to her bedside. Her face was gray, the color of the sheets and of her once dainty cotton nightdress with the high scalloped neckline. Surveying us with that narrowing of the eyes that betokened an important decision she said: "Girls, I've been awake most of the night thinking and I've decided that it's not fair to you to have to be cooped up in one room with a sick, poverty-stricken, useless old woman."

We started to protest as we always did, but she held up her hand for silence.

"If I could possibly afford it I would rent a little cottage by the seashore for a few weeks but I've taken all the principal I dare—if I take any more God knows what will become of us."

"Could Grandpa lend you the money for the cottage?" Rachel ventured.

"No, dear, Grandpa has spent all he should and more on me and my family. He has little more than what he earns and his earning powers aren't what they used to be. No, I can't do that. If I could *only* get my health and strength back I might be able to go back to teaching—in a private school where they take married women—but every time I think I'm better something comes up and I'm down and out again. Of course your father *should* support his family but what he sends me is barely enough for *one* person to keep body and soul together let alone four—either he can't or he won't send any more. I've threatened and threatened and nothing does any good. I lay awake here most of the night trying to think of some solution. Every way I turn I see no way out."

"Don't worry about us, Mother," Rachel said. "We're all right."

"Yes, we're all right," Phoebe and I echoed.

"No, it isn't fair to you. You're young and full of health and you deserve something better than this," motioning to the mussed beds carelessly strewn with our clothes of the day before. "So I have decided that as soon as the Flannagans are through with their breakfast I shall go downstairs and use their telephone and send your grandmother a telegram. I'm going to send you to Wychmere for a visit . . ."

"But, Mother," Rachel began, "I don't think Vicky will like . . ."

"Don't call that woman 'Vicky.' It's not a dignified name for a grandmother. It's typical of her to want to be called something so frivolous. I don't care whether she likes it or not," she continued grimly, "and I don't see how she can sit there in that beautiful place surrounded by luxury while her only son's children are living in poverty and squalor in the hot city all summer long. I don't think it will hurt her to do that much for them!"

Off we went, therefore, that very afternoon with our battered straw suitcase, in a taxi to North Station and the four-hour trip to Wychmere where we arrived in the late afternoon. Uncle Luke Appleton, Vicky's brother-in-law (we always called my grandmother 'Vicky' when we stayed with her, at her specific request, Mother's objections notwithstanding), was at the station to meet us and to drive us in Vicky's shining Model T Ford the mile and a half up the broad tree-lined Main Street to Pinewood.

Uncle Luke was a strikingly handsome old man, tall and slender with blue eyes, rosy cheeks, snow white hair and a Van Dyke beard. I remember little about him, for he died soon after, except that he and Aunt Frieda Appleton always ate breakfast in the kitchen because he "preferred" it that way and that he never drank coffee but always Postum and "cracked" cocoa. Once when I was a tiny girl he had made me a small wheelbarrow, exactly like his big one, painted blue, with "Amanda" in white letters on its side.

Aunt Frieda Appleton met us at the side door, a forbidding expression on her stern features.

"Girls," she hissed before we could set foot in the hallway, "you must be extremely quiet. Your grandmother is far from well. She simply must *not* be disturbed. She's asleep at last, thank heaven. I've been keeping the house quiet so she could get a little much needed rest. She's been dreadfully upset all day." Then with a nod toward the back stairs, "I'll show you to your rooms. I'm sorry to say, Uncle Luke and I are going out this evening, so I shall have to leave you. I presume, however," with a glance at my sister, "that you, Rachel, will see to it that your younger sisters are on their *very* best behavior."

"Yes'm," said Rachel and we filed silently up the back staircase.

Great Aunt Frieda was the eldest of the three Stuart sisters. Great Aunt Hester, the maiden lady, with whom my father had lived and gone to high school in Norwell, Massachusetts, was the middle sister, my grandmother the youngest. There were two brothers in the Stuart family, but like Mother's family, we hardly knew them. The sisters were the important people in our lives.

Aunt Frieda was a handsome, statuesque woman with a formidable bust which she held proudly up to its most prominent position. Her snow white hair piled high above her brows was, of course, done up in a generous pug on top of her head. Her face wore a customarily stern expression, her sizeable jaw clamped firmly into place to keep her false teeth from slipping.

Like her younger sisters, she had no formal schooling beyond high school; like them she had been forced because of her father's death to work as a secretary when she was very young, but she was extraordinarily well read and was always considered the scholar of the family.

Pinewood had been her home for many years now. The winter following my Uncle Thomas's death, when my grandmother had had her "nervous breakdown," she had come to take care of her, and she and Uncle Luke had moved in permanently. Unlike Grandfather Willard, Uncle Luke Appleton was "poor as Job's turkey," as my grandmother said, so it was a good arrangement for them and it suited my grandmother. Uncle Luke did all the heavy work of the place, with occasional help from a handyman, taking care of the coal furnace, doing the outside chores, running the car and keeping it in the pristine condition my grandmother required. In return my grandmother provided their dwelling and their food.

Although such an idea was never breathed, one had the feeling that the Appletons were in a somewhat subservient position at Pinewood. For years, ever since her breakdown, my grandmother had been treated like a semi-invalid. Her periodic attacks, of what precise nature no one seemed sure, would send her to bed for several days; the doctor would be summoned and everyone walked about the house on tiptoe speaking in hushed voices until she got up again, when she would spring back as lively and industrious as ever. Because of her "delicate" condition, or because the Appletons were dependent on her for her bounty, or perhaps because in her girlhood she had been the beauty of the family, my grandmother was queen in her household. Everything revolved around her.

Aunt Frieda showed us to our room and was in the act of tiptoeing to the door, her finger on her lips, when my grandmother called from her bedroom: "Frieda? Have the children come?"

"Yes, Victoria, but . . ." began Aunt Frieda but my grandmother interrupted her.

"Rachel! Girls! Come in, please. I want to see you."

We walked primly into her bedroom.

She looked picturesque lying on her blue chaise longue with her white hair and her pale lavender challis negligée. She had been in semimourning ever since the death of her husband many years before, wearing only black, white, black and white, or lavender.

"I'm very sorry, girls, that you find me indisposed," she said clearing her throat and turning her head languidly on her pillow, "I'm afraid you will have to have supper by yourselves. Aunt Frieda and Uncle Luke are dining out this evening and I have one of my horrid sick headaches." Then to Rachel, "You may sleep on the sleeping porch tonight. Your bed is ready and waiting as always—but," glancing at Phoebe and me, "you younger girls will have to sleep in the nursery. Minna hadn't enough notice to make up your beds outdoors. She has a delicious supper for you —clam chowder and blueberry muffins." Then dryly to me, "I expect you'll enjoy that, won't you, Amanda?" Before I had time to reply she turned again to Rachel. "Was it a tiring trip?"

"Oh no!" said Rachel.

"I love to ride on trains," Phoebe added.

"Well I'm glad you do, Phoebe. I detest the filthy things. There goes the supper bell now. You'd better run p.d.q. and wash your faces and hands. You must be dreadfully dirty, and please, girls," as we started from the room, "do try to keep the bathroom tidy. Alma has just this morning given it a good scrubbing."

Despite her periodic "spells" of sick headache and the like, Vicky, at this time not yet sixty years old, was an extraordinarily youthful, active person. Everyone around her admired her excessively, saying how beautiful she was.

Yet it was impossible for me to see anything remotely beautiful about her.

Undeniably in her youth she had been very pretty with abundant red-gold hair, brown eyes, vivid coloring, and a voluptuous figure. This was apparent from the many pictures of her on the walls and dressers in all the bedrooms at Pinewood. One in particular I admired, taken when she was twenty-five with the famous hair done in an elaborate French twist with a tortoise shell comb, one "love lock" springing from the top. She had saved her curls and occasionally showed them to us in their lavender tissue paper sheets inside a white box marked "Victoria's Hair—1883," just as she had saved Father's brown, Thomas's red, and Rachel's dark locks neatly done up and marked in similar boxes.

Now her hair was no longer gold but yellow white carefully arranged under a lavender net to cover the receding temples on her high forehead, with an intricate knot at the back enhanced by a switch made from her own hair years before; this switch when not on her head hung by the mirror of her dressing table and served as a favorite perch for her canary, Valentine, when she let him out directly after breakfast every morning for his exercise and bath.

The years had added fat to her features, which had never been distinguished or well defined like my mother's. Her eyes, yellow now instead of brown, were spoiled by the pince-nez she always wore. I hated pince-nez; they did such awful things to people's noses. Like Mother's, her eyes had the same penetrating expression when she was cross-questioning us or saying something funny, and she had a trick of dilating them in a comical way, but her remarks were usually caustic, her expression more shrewd than intelligent. Her figure, still good, was extremely erect, with narrow hips, nice legs, pretty shoulders, and a large bust.

"All the Stuart women have large busts" she used to say.

That evening after we three girls had had our supper, washed, and climbed into bed, Rachel on the porch, Phoebe and I in the nursery, my grandmother came to bid us good night.

"I hope you are quite comfortable," she said in her hoarse voice surveying Phoebe and me from the threshold as we lay in our immaculately clean beds.

"Oh yes," we replied eagerly, "very comfortable."

"That's good. Now sleep well and please remember, *no* talking, not even whispering. As you know, my chamber is next to yours and I don't care to have my rest disturbed by the sound of little girls talking and giggling. Good night. Sleep well." She leaned down and gave us each a quick peck on the cheek, snapped off the light, and shut the door.

Phoebe and I lay quietly in our beds and presently Phoebe was sound asleep. I was about to doze off too when I heard the sound of voices down the hall in my grandmother's upstairs sitting room. It was my grandmother and the Appletons who had just returned from their supper party. I could not make out what they were saying until Uncle Luke had said good night and gone upstairs and my aunt and my grandmother were approaching the door to the sitting room on their way to bed.

". . . absolutely the limit," Aunt Frieda was saying. "What *are* you going to do?"

"Don't fret about it, Frieda," my grandmother said crisply.

"But, sister! With everything you have to do this summer! It's the worst imposition I've ever known. As if they were *your* responsibility!"

Then there was a jumble of sounds as of my grandmother "tidying" the room before she retired.

". . . he'll be here tomorrow" I heard her say.

That was all except for the sound of her footsteps as she made her way down the hall to the bathroom.

In spite of the fact that there was no question in my mind as to who "they" were I was not unduly offended by the conversation. As I lay there in the deliciously cool room under the fragrant coverlets—everything at Pinewood smelled good—a feeling of pleasure and wonderment at the beauty and luxury of my surroundings crept over me. I had always loved this place. Everything about it was so perfectly appointed, so splendid, so larger than life, everything including its inhabitants was so awe-inspiring and a little frightening. When in the past I had come here I could never quite believe, after I had returned to Cambridge and our small, cramped rooms, that my visit had actually taken place. Pinewood was for me unreal, evanescent, a happy dream.

PINEWOOD

Pinewood had been built a number of years before the turn of the century by my grandparents as a summer place when they were a young, freshly married couple. The house was typical of summer houses of the period, a large square building of red stained shingles surrounded on three sides by wide verandahs, one of which was screened in for a summer sitting room below and a sleeping porch above.

The roof with wide overhanging eaves was surmounted by an enormous chimney painted white—the white of the chimney and the red of the house spectacular against the setting of lofty pines and gleaming birches. There were six or seven acres of grounds which seemed to me then like the country estates I had read about in Jane Austen's novels.

To the right of the house, as one faced it, was my grandmother's flower garden, which she cultivated herself, from which ran a pretty little path bordered by ferns and old-fashioned flowers which in turn led through a shady arbor of trees and vines to the farthest reach of the place where there was an extensive vegetable garden tended by Uncle Luke and a handyman. Vicky's table was abundantly supplied from this garden and from the numerous strawbery, raspberry, and blackberry bushes on the place; every summer Sunday she served strawberry or raspberry ice cream made with a hand freezer by Minna and Uncle Luke outside the kitchen door.

In front of the house was a sweep of lawn stretching to Main Street and thence to the mall (pronounced with a flat *a* by the townspeople), which ran down the middle of Main Street to the village. Every spring after the snow and ice had melted from under the last branch and the lawn restored to its customary perfection, wickets for croquet were set out on the right half of this lawn. My grandmother had been an expert player in her younger days and still loved to go out for a "round" before supper on summer evenings.

To the left of the house beyond another square of lawn, in the center of which stood a mighty black copper beech tree, was the long driveway leading to the garage and to the back door; this was lined with birches, pine trees, spruce, and hemlock, their branches forming a natural arch revealing a vista of forest beyond. The garage, at some distance from the house, contained Vicky's Model T

Ford, kept polished and shining by Uncle Luke and driven only by him until he died.

In a narrow shed adjoining the garage Uncle Luke, who was a skillful carpenter, kept his tools and on the walls the entire collection of license plates in two neat rows according to years starting with 1916. There was a smell about that garage and shed, a brew of freshly sawed wood, pipe tobacco, grease from the car, and powder from the huge grindstone mingled with whiffs of pine from the woods outside, which was particularly pleasing to my nostrils.

Behind the garage and through a wooded path was what was always called the "Boat House." It *had* been a boat house in its youth and had been moved from some lakeside by Father and Uncle Thomas as boys and set here as a retreat for themselves. Mother had told us that when they were first married Father had planned to use it as a summer cottage but this had never happened. For this reason, or perhaps because everything to do with my father's youth seemed romantic to me, I cherished a special feeling for the Boat House until I had a chance to examine it thoroughly. It proved a disappointment, being now a repository for things Father no longer cared about: two old canoes, odds and ends of furniture that had belonged to my parents' early married life, broken chairs, rusty bed springs, mice-inhabited mattresses. The Boat House was always kept locked, as was the garage at night; two heavy keys attached to wooden paddles marked "Boat House" and "Garage" hung on their hooks in the side hall.

The driveway turned right at the garage and continued to the back door where there was a turn-around. My grandmother never allowed us to use this door. It was reserved for delivery men and the servants; we used the side door as did Uncle Luke. Vicky and Aunt Frieda and visitors used the front door.

Behind the turn-around was the clothesyard, a wooden

platform with lines strung above it, used by the laundress and Minna and once a year on the Fourth of July by my grandmother, when she went out directly after breakfast to throw a few torpedoes, her only recognition of the holiday.

Beyond the clothesyard were the woods, kept like everything else at Pinewood in impeccable condition. Not a twig, not a dead leaf, never an unsightly scrap of paper was allowed to remain for more than an hour. Every morning my grandmother went out in good weather or bad to pick up and inspect. There were nothing but the magnificent pines interspersed with a few hemlock and spruce trees, and underneath, the spongy carpet of pine needles, broken here and there by clumps of wild berries and checkaberries, spicy and delicious.

It had been our delight when younger on our occasional summer visits to go out, Phoebe and myself, to make "fairy gardens" in these woods, an art taught us by Rachel from Great Aunt Frieda, who despite her formidable manner, specialized in "magic," playing the role of "fairy godmother" to her young niece. These little squares of pine needles decorated with live pine, spruce, boletus, and checkaberries, with their bright red fruit and shiny leaves, were peopled during the night by the fairies who danced in them and left some entrancing token of their gratitude to the architects.

Inside the house the furniture was a conglomeration of Victorian, early American, and what was then modern. The plan was an open one with the living room and dining room running the length and width of the house in the shape of an L. The black brickwork of the tremendous fireplace occupied the entire rear wall of the living room. There were oriental rugs, a grand piano, a large overstuffed antimacassared couch and chairs, massive tables and cabinets of cherry wood carved by Uncle Luke himself and highly esteemed by my grandmother, a giant grandfather's clock in the far corner, several immense jardinieres, two large potted ferns, and a good deal more of the same.

The remainder of the downstairs was dining room, butler's pantry, kitchen, and laundry. Upstairs were a sitting room, several elaborately furnished bedrooms and the maids' rooms.

The third floor, the attic, only partially finished, consisted of three rooms: a large bed-sitting room occupied by Aunt Frieda and Uncle Luke, the sewing room where Vicky kept all her materials including a bust of her own figure covered in black velvet, where Mrs. Springer came twice a year to make up dresses for her and Rachel and sometimes for Phoebe and me, and a large room in back devoted to countless richly bound volumes of Dickens, Thackeray, Meredith, Scott, Shakespeare, George Eliot, Victor Hugo, Jane Austen, the Brontes, Gibbon, Prescott, and many more.

This room was a favorite haunt of Rachel's and, whenever I visited there, of mine as well. I spent hours at a time, lying on my stomach gobbling down everything until my eyes smarted and my stomach groaned, so that when I stood up in reponse to my grandmother's bell (she was punctual to a fault about meal hours) I would almost keel over from dizziness.

A TRIP WITH FATHER

But the delights of Pinewood were not to be ours for long. The afternoon after our arrival Father appeared on the scene. Racing up the front staircase two steps at a time, more like a boy of fifteen than a man in his forties, he greeted us girls in his usual merry, offhand fashion, "Hello old socks," then proceeded to his mother's bedroom where she lay reading on her chaise longue.

"Hi there, Vicky, old top," he said, lightly dropping a kiss on her forehead. "Well, here I am!"

How well I recall the expression on my grandmother's face as she looked up at him over the tops of her pince-nez, a mixture of admiration—he was looking very dashing —and annoyance and something like amusement, as the twitching at the corner of her lip indicated. Presently we were dismissed from the room and a long conference took place.

We did not know until later that my grandmother had wired him as soon as she had Mother's telegram to say *she* was not well and could by no means have us all and that he had better do something about it *immediately*. All we knew was that early the next morning Father told us to get ready "pronto," we were to catch the first train to Portland for a day's outing. We asked no more but got ourselves together, excited at the prospect in spite of our vague feelings of guilt about Mother. We had never been anywhere with Father since their separation eight years before except on the walks around the block when he came to Cambridge to call.

Minna, the cook, packed up a little wicker hamper with delicious thinly sliced cucumber sandwiches and fragrant freshly baked ginger cookies, her specialty, and off we set on the train.

Father was in a gay mood. It reminded me of the old days when we lived in Brookline with him and Mother and he used to take us to the beaches nearby in his Stanley Steamer.

"Who knows what we have for lunch?" he asked us, his brown eyes glistening, as we settled ourselves in the coach seats opposite each other.

He's certainly very young looking, I thought, scrutinizing him when I thought he wasn't noticing. His skin was fresh and deeply tanned against his white shirt and black silk-knitted tie, the kind he always wore, his hair thick and glossy, and he had shaved off his mustache, a great improvement.

"I know," cried Phoebe, always the first to respond to his overtures.

"What then?"

"Why cucumber sandwiches! I saw Minna making them and ginger cookies—mmm," and she rolled her eyes and patted her stomach. Father pretended to be very solemn.

"Oh no, I think not. Those were for Vicky's luncheon. I believe we're having baked bean sandwiches. That's what I told Minna to make." He winked across at Rachel sitting beside me.

"Baked bean sandwiches!" chortled Phoebe. "Who ever heard of baked bean sandwiches!" Phoebe loved to laugh and was as willing to respond to Father as to anyone who amused her. I stared at him stonily.

"Of course." He grinned, delighted at Phoebe's merriment. "Cold baked bean sandwiches. They're my favorite. Don't you like them?"

"No—no," she sputtered happily. "Of course I don't like them—*cold* baked bean sandwiches! Oh my goodness!"

Rachel was smiling; I was glowering. Phoebe had held the stage long enough.

"And you, Amanda, don't you like baked bean sandwiches?" lifting an eyebrow in my direction.

"I've never had them."

Tempted as I was to join in the fun, none of it seemed amusing and I could think of nothing amusing to retort. It was my role, furthermore, in our family to play the clown; I resented Phoebe's taking over. He must have been offended by my negative response because after that he didn't address me again.

Broodingly contemplating the summer countryside, a shimmer of pale greens against the blacks of the pine trees, my thoughts threaded their way in and out, in and out, through the speeding landscape weaving a haphazard pattern, now through a clump of junipers, now a boulder squatting on the embankment, now an old gray farmhouse with its newly red silo, and here a broad blue expanse of Casco Bay. What kind of evergreen was it? . . . I wished I knew more about such things . . . How ignorant I was, compared to Rachel for instance who knew all about birds and flowers . . . When you came right down to it I didn't know much of anything . . . I wasn't a very *nice* person either—so jealous, *wretchedly* jealous and disagreeable at times, as just now because Father found Phoebe amusing . . . Why *wouldn't* he adore Phoebe? . . . She was so loving with *everyone* . . . Why couldn't I be like that? . . . I wanted to . . . What would it be like to hurl oneself from the train? . . . Crashing perhaps against that rock! Ugh! Horrible! . . . Best not to think such thoughts . . . Would anyone, except Mother of course, care if I were dead? . . .

What a lonely looking house . . . What did people who lived there do all day way out here? . . . I couldn't imagine living there . . . But a big city like New York would be worse . . . Did Father like living there? Going to the opera, living with "that woman"? . . . He *seemed* jolly enough . . . But *was* he really? . . . Did he miss us at *all?* . . . How beautiful it was in Maine! . . . How I loved the ocean! Plunging into its foaming waves . . . And Nantasket Beach . . . How far away it seemed and how far away Mother in Cambridge in that hot messy little room . . . sitting there this very minute no doubt—alone—smoking her powder and gasping for breath and thinking of us probably. All at once tears were thick on my lashes and I had to pretend to see something the train had left far behind.

Now the train was slowing down for Old Orchard and we girls began to gather up our things, happy at the prospect of a day at the beach. But before we could get to our feet, Father said in his usual peremptory fashion: "Sit down, please."

We obeyed like lightning. The train lurched off again. We were utterly mystified. Presently Rachel plucked up her courage to say in her clear cultivated voice "Where are we going, Father?"

He wasn't annoyed as I half expected but reached out a hand and patted her shoulder.

"Don't worry, old scout. Everything's fine. I'm just taking you on a little trip. That's all. You leave it to me."

So we settled down again, everyone quiet. Father made no further efforts toward conversation, but took some papers from his waistcoat pocket and proceeded to bury himself in his own thoughts while we dared not chatter and giggle as we might have without him.

Thus we rode for a long stretch in complete silence. Then he rose abruptly, stretched his long lean body—I can see him now, his back arched, his broad shoulders raised, the dark hair springing back from his high forehead, the muscles of his jowls taut—and jerked the little wicker hamper from the rack overhead.

"Well, boys," he announced, "Time for chow!"

We ate our delicious cucumber sandwiches and ginger cookies, washed down with water from the cooler, but the festive mood had gone.

On we went past Kennebunk, Kennebunkport, Portsmouth, Newburyport, until we reached the North Station, where Father whisked us with our old straw suitcase (which he must have stored in the vestibule of the train for it was the first time we had seen it) into a taxi and across the city to South Station so quickly that we had no time to think.

Then came another train trip, even longer than the first, and another picnic of Minna's remaining cucumber sandwiches and ginger cookies. At last we arrived late at night at our destination. This proved to be Riverton, New Jersey, where we were met by an attractive youngish man, introduced to us as "Mr. Smith," and taken to a wooden station wagon, the first of its kind I had ever seen.

His good humor having returned, Father talked and laughed with Mr. Smith in the front seat while Rachel and I in back with Phoebe between us exchanged worried hand squeezes. Mr. Smith's friendly remarks tossed over his shoulder fell on barren ground. Even Phoebe's blithe mood had vanished.

At length we turned off the highway onto a dirt road and after what seemed like an endless series of buckings and jerkings, drew up at an unimposing camplike building in the middle of a field broken only by occasional scrubby bushes. The door to the camp was immediately thrown open revealing the figure of a woman against the dim light of a kerosene lamp. I had never seen her before, but I knew instantly, as did Rachel and Phoebe, who she was and why she was there.

We had always known about Father's mistresses. The first one, Grace Viles, I remember the best (though I never met her), because Mother talked about her the most, saying among other things that Father sang "Annie Laurie" to her. "Throat like a swan!" Mother had sneered bitterly. "More like an old yellow hen's." Grace Viles had been the cause of several nightmares when I was five or six. The long scraggly yellow neck would coil up out of the darkness, an evil face would leer at me, and I would wake up screaming for Mother or Bridget.

It was quite apparent that the grinning woman on the threshold was another one.

"So! You are here at last!" she exclaimed in a thick German accent. "Come in! Come in! I haf everything ready for you."

"This is Eva, girls," said Father lightly, "camp cook and bottle washer, eh Eva?" but this failed to deceive any of us, even Phoebe who shrank when Eva stooped down to help her off with her jacket. Eva was too familiar, too jolly with Mr. Smith and Father to be a mere bottle washer.

The thing that surprised us about her was that she was young, in her twenties I estimated from her smooth skin, abundant blonde hair, and quick youthful laugh. It was impossible to judge her figure because of the loose fitting smock she wore. Her face, round and flat with a rather protuberant lower jaw, was not at all distinguished or pretty except when she smiled, which she did much of the time; then her blue eyes became bluer and her large wide mouth shot up at the corners producing a merry, comical look that dispelled her plainness.

All three—Mr. Smith, Father, and Eva—laughed a great deal and said things which meant nothing to us and presently Mr. Smith left and we three girls, having declined

Eva's offer of cold cereal and milk, went to bed exhausted.

We woke to brilliant sunshine and overpowering heat. Father had risen early, as he always did, and had gone off with Mr. Smith to take the commuter's train to New York City, where he and Mr. Smith, Eva explained, worked in the same advertising firm.

"It is nice—yah?—they can work together—your father and his friend?"

After breakfast Eva took us into Father's studio, directly adjoining the kitchen, to show us his paintings, undoubtedly in an effort to divert us, but it was not a success. We were shocked.

The large unframed oil paintings crowding the room, on the walls, on the floor, on an easel by the window, were all of the same subject: a nude young woman, very fully formed, with large hips and buttocks, large stomach, and most shocking, very large breasts with enormous dark nipples, in every conceivable posture, standing by a couch her arms upstretched, sitting on a stool drying her hair, reclining on her side under a tree, crouching by the edge of a brook. Although the young woman's body was fully exposed, every portion well highlighted, in each painting the head was drawn in such a way that the face was obscured by a shadow, the fall of her hair or the curve of her arm.

Rachel and Phoebe and I stood there embarrassed, not knowing what to say. We had never seen a woman naked before—Mother never undressed in our presence—and this woman was *so* naked.

"They are very beautiful, yes?" Eva said, but sensing our embarrassment, perhaps, she did not wait for an answer. "Now I do some work, girls, and you must go to explore. Then maybe later we have a good time. Yah?"

As we were quitting the studio Rachel nudged me and glanced significantly in the direction of one corner where far back almost out of sight was a small delicately painted watercolor in an oval frame of a young woman in a canoe, the paddle resting athwart the beams steadied by her graceful brown arms, her light brown hair and white muslin dress, in the style of the early 1900's, gently billowing in the breeze. It was Mother. There was something so subtly eager and joyful about the face and figure that I knew at once what she had meant when she called Father's earlier paintings "wistful."

Eva allowed us a moment to look saying, "That is nice too," then firmly shut the studio door.

After aimlessly exploring the surrounding fields, the only notable feature of which were countless giant-sized mosquitos, we three wandered down the dirt road well away from the camp. Here we held a conference. The situation was unbearable.

"Listen, kids," Rachel whispered, "I'm going to try to get to the town, the one we went through last night, I think I can find it, and mail a postcard to Mother—I know she won't like our being here—and tell her we want to go home."

"Good!" I said "I'll come with you."

"Me too," said Phoebe.

"No, you mustn't. If you do, that girl will get suspicious and tell Father. You realize, kids, that he has *kidnapped* us!" Rachel's brown eyes held an expression remarkably like Mother's.

"But why?" I gasped. It was like something out of Robert Louis Stevenson!

"I don't know," said my sister mysteriously, half enjoying the drama of the situation, and she sneaked off down the hot dusty road.

While she was gone we had a visitor at the camp, a small boy younger than Phoebe, who was introduced to Phoebe and me as "Thomas." Eva gave us all cookies and ginger ale and sent us out to play again. Standing on a rock a little distance from the camp we conversed with Thomas in a desultory manner.

"What's your name?" Thomas asked me.

"Amanda Evans Willard."

"And what's hers?"

"Phoebe Stuart Willard," said Phoebe who needed no one to speak for her.

"My name's Thomas Willard Merrill" the boy announced. Phoebe and I looked at each other in astonishment.

"Isn't that man your father, the one who met us at the bus last night with *my* father?" I demanded.

"Yes, of course," was the reply.

"Then your name is Thomas *Smith*" I said.

"It is *not*. My name is Thomas Willard Merrill and my father's name is Jerome Wilson Merrill." He turned on his heel disgustedly and ran off across the field.

Meanwhile Rachel had walked the hot dusty two or three miles to the little town of South Riverton, had succeeded in finding the post office and sending a hastily scribbled card to Mother in Cambridge.

We spent another night at the camp and another long uneventful day. Had there been anything exciting to do, a place to swim, for instance, we might have been more complaisant about it all, but there was nothing. Father was off in the city all day, Thomas did not come to see us again, and Eva seemed endlessly busy about the camp.

Actually, although we would never have admitted it, we were all three tempted to like Eva. She was a pleasant sort of person offering to do what she could to amuse us in this out-of-the-way place. Occasionally she and Phoebe sat down for a game of hearts or checkers but Rachel and I, coldly polite, continued to resist her overtures.

Early in the morning of the third day a car drove up with a telegram for Father (there was no telephone in the camp) sent by Mother, she told us later, demanding that we girls be returned at once or she would start legal proceedings. Father, I am sure, was relieved to have us go, for without more ado we were ordered to pack our few belongings and sent off to the station in a taxi.

Mother and Cambridge looked wonderful to us after South Riverton, New Jersey. The hot spell had let up, Mother had sufficiently rallied from her latest bout to clean our room and kitchenette, and the first evening home she took us to the Dupont Restaurant and the Bijou Dream Theatre. Throughout the evening she was her old gay self, but the instant we set foot in our room after the walk from the streetcar, her gaiety vanished and she began to grill us intensively about every detail of our trip, especially the visit to New Jersey and more particularly Eva. What did she look like?

"She was hideous," I declared. "Wasn't she, Rachel?"

"We-ell not exactly that," said Rachel who was scrupulously honest, sometimes to the point of tactlessness, "but certainly not at all attractive."

"Attractive! She was the *worst* looking thing I've ever seen. And she talked like this" and I produced a caricature of Eva's accent.

"And she did *this*," added Phoebe thrusting out her lower jaw in an exaggerated imitation of Eva's less fortunate feature.

"That's what the country people in Nova Scotia used to call a 'jimber jaw'. It's the mark of a degenerate!" Mother pronounced.

"I hated her" I cried passionately. "She was awful! I don't see how Father can *like* her. Why *does* he?"

"Heaven only knows why that man is the way he is," Mother said glumly. "He was born that way I guess, or maybe it was his upbringing—probably both. He's been like that as long as I've known him—completely amoral.

But *this* takes the cake! Taking his own children into a house with that *creature!* You'd think he'd be ashamed to have you see him with such a person! You'd think such a woman would repel him. But no, he seems to single out that kind. The uglier and coarser the better. It makes no difference to him who or what they are—young, old, beautiful, ugly, black, white."

"Black!" Rachel exclaimed.

"Yes. Black or white, it makes no difference. Anything at all to satisfy his ego. How old is this person?"

"Oh—just sort of old," I said.

"Oh, no, Mandy," Rachel interposed. "She *isn't* old."

"How old?" Mother's eyes flashed threateningly.

"I'm—not sure," said Rachel quickly retreating.

"And in one of the rooms there were pictures of ladies all *bare!*" volunteered Phoebe.

"I see," said Mother grimly. "Just what I expected. That woman is his model. They usually are."

Rachel and I exchanged glances. Of course! That's exactly what she was. We knew a good deal about artists and models from *Trilby* and *Little Billee.*

"There was a picture of you, Mother, in a white dress . . ." Rachel began.

"I don't want to hear a word about his paintings," Mother interrupted, her voice trembling with fury. "They are immoral! Degenerate!"

"But that one of you was nice . . ." faltered Rachel.

"Not another word!" But after a moment when Rachel turned away, her eyes filling with tears, Mother held out her arms to her. "It's all right, dearie, it's all right," she said gently.

Then Phoebe told Mother about Thomas Willard Merrill.

"Aha! That's interesting," said Mother, then looking at

each of us intently. "You know who his father *is*, don't you?"

"Isn't he the man who went with you and Father and Uncle Thomas on your honeymoon?" asked Rachel.

"Exactly. He's Jerry Merrill."

"But why did Father say his name was Smith?" I asked. Mother shook her head sadly.

"I suppose Jerry didn't want me to know he was in on this affair. Jerry's a decent person. But he's weak. He'll go along with anything your Father proposes. He's always been like that. But we used to be such good *friends*. I wouldn't have thought Jerry would be part of this—this—" For a moment she couldn't go on. I thought she was going to cry but her lips tightened. "I suppose he thought it was a great joke—just one of Archie's boyish pranks," she added bitterly.

The talk went on late into the night.

"It's very important, girls, very important, that you tell me every *word* that passed between that woman and your father."

Anxious to do our part—Rachel had been highly commended for her courage and ingenuity in getting the message through to Mother, "like the message to Garcia,"—Phoebe and I proceeded to relate everything we could remember.

The evening before we had left the camp, after we three girls had gone to bed, I had lain awake listening to Father and Eva laughing and talking in the kitchen. Their voices had been indistinct and the only phrase I had actually caught was something from Eva about having to "buy a black corset." Reconstructing it now, I suppose she was referring to the difficulties of doing laundry in the primitive little camp. Mother seized on this fiercely.

"Amanda, do you know what they were talking about?" Her eyes black with anger burned straight into me.

"No," I quavered.

"They were talking about my *death!*" There was a triumphant ring to her voice.

"Oh no, I don't think so. They were laughing and joking all the while."

"Yes. Laughing and joking. I have no doubt they were. About me, don't you see? They're waiting for me to die so they can be married. This is the *mourning* she'll wear to my funeral!" There was such bitterness to her look and tone I felt sick inside. "You don't know your father. That's the kind of thing that would amuse him. Oh yes!"

Shocked at such a suggestion, we all three did our best to refute it, but Mother would not be denied and proceeded to question and counter question me as to every word and look that had passed between Father and Eva.

"Good for you, Mandy, to remember it all so clearly! What else did she say? And your father? What did he say? Try to remember. This may be vitally important to us all!"

Having made the initial disclosure I was carried along with the drama of it all until I suddenly discovered, to my utter horror, that I was improvising. And I couldn't stop. The more questions Mother shot at me, the more I improvised. At last it became apparent to us both that I was fabricating.

"Amanda, would you get up on the stand before a judge and jury in a courtroom and *swear* that your father and this woman said these things?" she said solemnly, giving me a look that seemed to penetrate to my very soul. "Would you repeat word for word what you have told me here tonight?" she continued relentlessly, "swearing on the Holy Bible to tell the whole truth and nothing but the truth?"

I nodded feebly.

"Are you positive, Amanda? If you lie in court you are

committing *perjury!* You realize *that*, do you not?" There
was no escaping the keen blue eyes.

"Yes, I'm positive." But my voice was a squeak.

"Very well, I shall take this to court. To the *highest*
court in the land if need be! This is *treachery*, perfidy of
the worst kind! Make no mistake about *that!*"

Trembling with anxiety I went to bed that night, sure
that I was to be summoned forthwith, the very next day
perhaps, to the highest court in the land. But nothing more
came of it. Mother never did take it to court nor was she
able to wreak vengeance on Father and Eva. One thing,
however, she did accomplish. After three or four con-
science-stricken days and sleepless nights I had learned my
lesson. I never lied to my mother again.

RACHEL

At the end of that summer the blow which Mother had so
long been dreading finally struck. We came in one afternoon to find her sitting in her rocking chair, a letter in her
hand, her cheeks pink with excitement.

"Just read this!" she said, disdainfully flinging the letter
to Rachel. "Read it aloud. I want your sisters to hear it."

Rachel read, her voice trembling:

" 'Dear Liza, I am sorry indeed to hear that you have
been having a bad time again with your asthma. It's most
unfortunate your doctor isn't able to help you. Is it possible

that you should try another man? A specialist perhaps who knows the latest remedies for bronchial ailments . . .' "

"Remedies for bronchial ailments!" snorted Mother. She hated having her asthma reduced to the indignity of bronchitis. She signaled for Rachel to proceed.

" 'It disturbs me to hear that you are in such poor health and the matter I am about to bring up has a direct bearing on this. It has been my idea for some time now that I might be able to help the situation by offering to send Rachel to boarding school. I have been giving this a great deal of thought and it seems to me that, although you would miss her of course, considering your poor state of health, it might make the burden lighter if you were to have two girls instead of three to look out for. As for Rachel herself, I'm sure you will agree with me that she is now at the age, about to enter secondary school, where she should have as many opportunities as possible to develop her fine mind and her many talents.

" 'I have an excellent school in mind, Deering Academy, in Portland, Maine, not too far away so she could be a five-day boarder, coming here on the weekends, and could continue to share her vacations with you and her sisters and with me in Wychmere.

" 'Will you give this matter your consideration and let me know as soon as possible so I can make arrangements for the coming year? Of course it goes without saying that I will undertake all expenses in connection with it including uniforms, allowances, etc.

" 'With very best wishes to you and the girls I remain as always, yours very truly, Victoria Stuart Willard.' "

When Rachel had finished she looked at Mother anxiously, uncertain of what her reaction might be.

"Well?" said Mother. "Isn't that exactly what I've always said about that woman? Isn't it?"

"But, Mother . . ." Rachel began.

"You see? All this talk about my being sick— Oh she knew when to jump in and take advantage of my mistake . . ."

"But, Mother," cried Phoebe running to Rachel and throwing her arms around her, "I don't want Rachie to go away—I don't want her to . . ."

Mother jumped up and putting her hand on her heart paced up and down the floor of our small room, her jaws tightly clenched as if in frightful pain.

"Mother, dear—*please* don't get so upset," Rachel begged.

"I think it's horrible of her to take Rachie away from us," I scowled. "She has no right to do such a thing. Rachel isn't *her* child!" Returning to her chair Mother gathered us around her.

"Girls," she spoke solemnly, enunciating each word as if it were a speech which she had rehearsed many times and was now delivering to a large audience instead of just us three sitting at her feet, "your grandmother *has* a right, a *legal* right to send Rachel to a boarding school of *her* choosing. That was written into the separation agreement between your father and me. But does she have a *moral* right? *That's* the question. Would any court in the land, any judge or jury, if I chose to contest that clause in the agreement, deny *me* the right to decide my own daughter's education, particularly in the light of what happened this summer? Your grandmother was the *cause* of your father's taking you, with no word to me, to that camp of his with his *mistress!* I doubt if *any* court after hearing that would deny me the right to break that clause in the agreement." She sighed heavily and thought for a moment while we waited for her to finish. "But the trouble is—and your grandmother is well aware of it—I have no money to undertake litigation. I have *known*, for years, of course I have known, that this was going to happen—but I didn't think it would come quite so soon." Then to herself, "Oh God! not quite so soon!" and she leaned her forehead on her hand, almost transparent now in its delicacy.

"But, Mother, I'm not *going* to leave you," Rachel said stoutly. "I have something to say about this and I'm not going to leave you, ever!" Mother took a handkerchief from her bathrobe pocket, blew her nose vigorously, and wiped her eyes.

"Yes, Rachel dear, you are—some day you must—but not right now, dear God. I thought they would wait until my death, but," she continued sternly, "you see, don't you, what has happened? Oh yes, they are going to prove that I am *incompetent!* Yes, yes," brushing aside our attempts to remonstrate, "this is the result of my rash action this summer when I sent that telegram and sent you girls down there. This is what they are doing to me now. That was where I made my mistake. I should have known—I *did* know—that I would be made to suffer for that."

"What do you mean?" I looked into her face.

"Amanda, *never* act impetuously as I did this summer in sending my children—and you are *my* children, never forget that—away from their own legal residence. I thought she might take care of you for a little while, that it would be good for you to be in that beautiful place, away from the heat and dirt of the city, but look what's happened! That woman is trying, has always wanted, and now she's bound and determined, even though she *knows* how much I depend on her, to take Rachel away from me."

"Oh, Mother," protested Rachel, "I don't think so, honestly I don't. I think she's just trying to do something for me—really . . ." But Mother held up her hand and Rachel knew she must be still.

"Rachel, girls," turning to include Phoebe and me, "make no mistake. Your Grandmother Willard is—what her own cousin said about her many years ago and I've *never* forgotten it. She's a drop of poison in the cup! That's what her cousin, Rachel Stuart—you're named after her, Rachel—said to me when I was a young woman, as fresh and trusting as you are now, girls. She said to me—and it was the only time I ever heard her utter a single unkind word against anyone: 'Eliza, beware of Victoria, she can be very charming when she chooses, but she's, never forget it,—she's a drop of poison in the cup!' "

A chill went through me at her words and the expression in her eyes, as it always did when she talked this way.

"I didn't know then," she went on, "what Cousin Rachel meant, but soon, oh very *soon*, I knew all right!"

"What did she *do?*" I said.

"It was more what she didn't do. Never once did she take my side, when even her own sister, Hester, was outraged and my father who is the most forgiving man who ever lived and *wanted* to like Archie . . . she did nothing, *nothing* I tell you to support me!"

"But what could she do?" Rachel asked.

"She could have taken me and my little girls into her house now and then when I was down and out, could have stood up for me to your father and to other people. Instead of that she said terrible things behind my back, belittling me, undermining me, even to my own family, when he had behaved so abominably, had committed a crime, yes a crime, against his entire family!"

"What crime?" I breathed.

Mother sat staring at me for a moment, then she drew a deep heavy sigh.

"Amanda, there are some things that, grown up as you are, you girls, you cannot—shouldn't even try to understand."

"We can understand, can't we Rachel?" I said.

"And I can understand too," cried Phoebe.

"Please tell us, Mother," Rachel said gently. "I think we should know these things."

"Well, I think I've told you girls—I *know* I've told Rachel—that not long after our return from London when Phoebe was not yet two years old I went to the hospital with a miscarriage—I've explained to you about miscarriages. I was dreadfully upset about losing that baby. It was a boy."

"Oh, I didn't know *that*," said Rachel. "How sad."

"Yes, it was. I felt especially sorry for your father. He'd wanted a boy so badly. But that didn't—couldn't account for what he did . . ."

"What *did* he do?" I said.

Mother sat for a long moment thinking, then she spoke slowly, abstractedly, as if we weren't there at all.

"While I was in the hospital he was unfaithful to me. He had been many times before, but this . . ." she stopped for a moment as if she were thinking back to that unhappy time, "this was the worst of all."

"While you were in the hospital! And you'd just lost your baby! Oh I think that's horrible!" cried Rachel. "How could he *do* that?"

"Rachel, my dearest child, little do you know—you think me bitter and unreasonable about him and his mother—but little do you know—God forgive me for telling you mean and sordid things about him—but they are nothing—nothing . . ." She broke off and put her eyes in her hand, then with a quick change of tone, her eyes flashing, "and when I found out about it and left him, your grandmother telephoned my sister, Hildred, and tried to blame *me* for what had happened, said that it was *my* fault, that I never should have married him in the first place, that I was older and should have known better, that he was nothing but a boy—and even after I had forgiven him and taken him back once more—which was what he wanted— she *continued* to malign me behind my back. *That* is what I can never forgive!" Then turning to us swiftly, accusingly, "Do you blame me?"

"No, of course we don't," Phoebe said quickly.

"And you, Rachel, and Amanda? Do you blame me? Tell me."

"No," said Rachel.

"No, of course not," I said.

During that night I was aware of Mother's getting up from the bed she and I shared to sit in her rocking chair coughing and burning her powder and rocking, rocking far into the night. When toward dawn she came back to bed at last, I was awakened by her sobbing and once I heard her moan, "My baby!" and I put my arms around her to comfort her. I knew she was talking about Rachel.

The next afternoon, however, when we came home from playing with some of our friends her manner was completely altered. She met us at the door with a letter in her hand—she was up and dressed for the first time in days, in her old black suit and the hat with the pompoms.

"I'm going out to post this," she said briskly. "I'll be back directly." And although we offered to take it for her she declined. When she returned she drew us around her again and as solemnly and dramatically as before said, "Girls, I prayed to God last night to help me to do the right thing and I have made my decision. I have just written to your grandmother and given my consent!"

"But, Mother," cried Rachel "I don't want to leave you! I don't want to leave you!" and Rachel who seldom cried burst into floods of tears.

After Mother had calmed her she spoke quietly, dispassionately: "Rachel, my dearest, you *do* want to go to school, I know, and in my heart of hearts I know it's right for you. Your grandmother *has* done some very cruel things to me, but I believe she means to help you and you deserve to go. It isn't right that because of things that have happened in the past I should stand in the way of it. So, please, say no more about it. Let's pluck up our courage and do what we both know should be done. You will come home often—for vacations—and Amanda and Phoebe here will be my little standbys while you are gone."

So the decision was made and in the middle of September Rachel packed Mother's best suitcase with her few belongings and set off on the train for Deering Academy.

PARTIES

Everything seemed strange after Rachel had gone. Although she had spent most of her spare time with her friends, the Whitmans, she had always been on hand to strengthen and support Mother, to comfort Phoebe, or to cajole me out of my dark moods. It was many weeks before we could get used to being without her.

I was thirteen now and in the eighth grade and Phoebe eleven and in the sixth. Mother had always worried that Rachel didn't have enough social life and now she worried about Phoebe and me.

"It's part of a young woman's education to go to parties," she said, "and you, Amanda, will be in high school next year. You should be learning to get along with boys at dances and things."

Phoebe was pining to go to dancing school; although Mother loved to dance herself and was keen to have us all go, the cost of three girls had been prohibitive. "If I can't send you all I won't send one," she said. The winter before Phoebe had had an experience which had upset Mother as much as it had Phoebe.

She had arrived home from school one afternoon in a state of wild excitement bearing a printed invitation to attend the annual party of Miss Carruther's Dancing Class at the First Congregational Church in Cambridge as a "guest of Miss Carolyn Watson."

On the occasions when Phoebe had spent the night at Carolyn Watson's house, a great treat, she found herself particularly fascinated by Mr. Watson, not so much for his personality which was stolid and uninspiring, as for his habit of polishing all the children's shoes every night after they went to bed. This struck Phoebe as the height of paternal devotion, something she longed for.

Mother, thrilled as Phoebe with the invitation, pulled herself together after a particularly ferocious attack of asthma and struggled into town in the icy weather on the streetcar the next morning to buy Phoebe some scarlet taffeta material for a party dress which she set to work to "run up" on her Singer that very evening.

With a mixture of envy and admiration, I watched Phoebe as she set forth on the afternoon of her party looking like a picturebook child in the red taffeta frock, her yellow curls bobbing under her perky Scotch cap.

She had gone off rosy and smiling and she came home that night tear streaked and forlorn to tell us the story. She had reached the church bursting with anticipation. At last her dream of dancing school had come true! Sure enough there was her friend, Carolyn, and the other little girls dressed in their best party dresses with hair ribbons to match and the little boys in dark blue suits with white gloves, all sitting on long benches along the side of the hall. The music commenced, Miss Carruthers stepped to the center of the hall and gave the signal, everyone rose, Phoebe among the first to hop to her feet and spring eagerly onto the floor for the one-two-three slide which she had learned from Mother when she was only three years old, but before she could take a step Miss Carruthers bounded up, she was sorry but visitors were *not* permitted to take part in the dancing, were only to watch and Phoebe must return to the bench.

So Phoebe, who was as graceful as a fairy, sat on her bench while the music played and the other children plodded around the hall. Nor did the ice cream and cake during the intermission make up for this deprivation and soon after that she made her way sadly home on the street-car.

Mother had been very sympathetic about Phoebe's disappointment and had said that as soon as she could "scrape together" the money she would send her to dancing school but other expenses had come along like buying clothes for us for school and doctors' bills and she wasn't able to do it.

That fall Aunt Hildred, Mother's older sister, called her one day and offered to try to get Phoebe and me into the Cambridge Skating Club. We had gone to the skating club once as Aunt Hildred's guests and had skated around the edges while the other children played hill-dill-come-over-the-hill-or-else-I'll-catch-you-standing-still and we had decided it wasn't much fun but we didn't like to tell Mother that. She was so happy with Aunt Hildred's offer. As it turned out, we never did join the club; it was just too expensive.

Then in October I was invited to a Halloween party. We had never been allowed to dress up and roam the streets on that evening; our activities had been confined to bobbing apples in a basin on the kitchen floor. So it was a real event to be asked to a Halloween party by a friend of mine,

Pinky Whittemore, a new girl in our class whose father was a professor at Harvard.

The fact that Phoebe was invited also delighted me; I was protective of my little sister and loved to feel that I was responsible for her, but when Mother proposed that I should also ask Pinky to include Aunt Hildred's son, Rupert, I was dismayed.

"He won't want to go to *that*," I said scornfully. "He's too old."

"Nevertheless, Amanda, I should like to have you ask Pinky to have him. An extra boy is always welcome at a party. He's your first cousin, your aunt has done a kindness to me in trying to get you girls into the skating club, she knows how I worry about you, and this is something we can do for her son."

So there was nothing for it but I must ask Pinky, who was agreeable about this as about everything, and to my surprise Rupert said he would come.

My cousin Rupert was a year and a half older than I. Although I had always admired him from afar, on the few occasions when our mothers were together, we had never had anything at all to say to each other. He could not be described as a handsome boy but his figure, like the rest of the Evans family, was slight and well knit and there was about his small dark face a mischievous, elfin quality that was very appealing. Habitually joking and laughing, he liked to tease us girls in a light-hearted way which we secretly enjoyed though of course we pretended to be annoyed.

The atmosphere in our room at Sacramento Street the evening of the party was one of unusual festivity. I hadn't seen Mother as happy in a long time. She had spent the day cleaning the place in anticipation of Rupert's call—he was to pick us up—and was now busy putting the finishing touches to our costumes. After countless days of indecision we were finally arrayed, Phoebe as a gypsy in the red taffeta of the winter before with red berries in her hair (like Babbie in *The Little Minister* Mother said) and I, a trifle uneasy as to the suitability of it, though Mother insisted I looked "very distinguished," in her college cap and gown.

With a flourish of the Flannagan's side doorbell Rupert arrived in a voluminous black cloak, hood, and mask. Mother greeted him cordially at the door to our kitchenette and, after the exchange of a few civilities, we three set off on the long walk to Pinky's house in Shady Hill, Phoebe and I trembling with anticipation.

We were the first guests to arrive. I introduced Rupert to Pinky, exactly as Mother had instructed me, "the gentleman *to* the lady first *always*," and we were seated on a sunporch adjoining the living room. It was a cold, rather grimy room with wicker furniture and one dimly naked light bulb suspended from the ceiling.

"We're just waiting 'til the others get here" I whispered to Phoebe and Rupert who raised his black eyebrows in a question mark while Phoebe sat crestfallen staring through the windows into the brightly lighted living room.

But we continued to sit there and the other guests who came dribbling in sat with us. Pinky greeted each new guest smilingly and soon everyone had assembled and sat around the walls of the sunroom waiting eagerly for the great moment when the doors would be thrown open, perhaps to a burst of music from the piano which we could glimpse through the curtains, to a living room, no doubt glowing with an open fire, and *certainly* festooned with orange crepe paper, to be greeted by a charming father and mother who after we had shaken hands—"no curtseying, girls, it's ungraceful"—would lead us through games of cobweb, bobbing for apples and maybe charades (if they realized how sophisticated some of the guests were). But no. We sat where we were on the cold, cheerless sunporch. Not a festoon, not a cobweb, not an apple.

After an hour or more of sitting, our teeth chattering, with slowly diminishing enthusiasm for the wonders of each other's costumes, the door to the living room was opened at last by Pinky's sister who quickly shut it again and silently came forward to pass us cold doughnuts and warm cider.

I couldn't believe it. I knew too much from Mother's stories about the jolly times in her youth and from parties in the "Our Gang" comedies to consider this proper hospitality. I was embarrassed too on account of Rupert, that my party was such a failure. Certainly he did his best to liven things up by teasing Pinky and Phoebe and me, but the sunporch was a poor background for any real hilarity and Pinky, who would have been an indifferent hostess under the most felicitous circumstances, appeared as uncomfortable as the rest of us.

Toward the end of the evening it occurred to me that Pinky's parents might be saving a surprise for the last moment when we would all burst in for a final treat, though it seemed to me, as I sat in my cold dark corner that this was certainly not the best way of running a party —such a waste of precious time.

But nothing of the kind happened. The Whittemores never even glanced out of the window at our beautiful costumes, and after one more imploring glance at the closed door and the bright window we made our departure.

We three walked in silence as far as Everett Street where Rupert was to spend the night with a friend. On the corner under the street lamp we paused for a moment.

"Are you kids going to be at Grandpa's for Thanksgiving this year?"

"I don't think so," I said dully, "we never do."

"I know. Why not?" His sharp eyes examined my face.

"Oh I dunno. Some long story about Aunt Belle," I replied indifferently, too dispirited to keep up my good manners any longer.

"That Aunt Belle! She must have been *bats*—bats in the belfry!" Rupert shook his head disgustedly. "Well good night, kids. Thanks for the party," and he was gone.

I knew as I watched his retreating figure that it would be a long time before he went anywhere with *us* again.

EVENINGS AT SACRAMENTO STREET

Now that Rachel had gone I had become Mother's chief support and confidant. During that winter I came to know her and appreciate her as one friend knows and appreciates another. She was good company. That she was a great talker herself did not prevent her from being responsive to whatever I might have to say. She was always ready to laugh at my witticisms.

"Amanda, you *are* funny," she would say with her odd throaty chuckle, "you remind me so much of my sister, Belle."

I particularly remember one day when I had stayed home from school because of a cold. Mother and I began talking after breakfast, about nine o'clock, and when it finally occurred to us that it might be lunch time we discovered to our amazement that it was four o'clock in the afternoon. Neither of us had noticed the passage of seven hours.

Every evening after I had finished my homework we sat late into the night reading and talking, she in her rocking chair, I close by lying on her bed, Phoebe asleep on the other side of the room in the bed she and I shared now that Rachel had gone.

One night, determined to find out some of the things I had never understood, I asked Mother the question all of us had asked so many times before:

"Why is Father such a bad person? What *makes* him that way, I mean?"

"He isn't *all* bad, Amanda. You mustn't think that. He has many good qualities. I suppose if one were charitable one would say that this weakness of his is something he can do nothing about." She gazed into the distance, her eyes sombre. "But that doesn't make it any easier for the people he hurts. I used to feel sorry for him, to think that if I loved him enough I could help him to overcome some of these things. But I couldn't. He doesn't *want* to be any different. No one can help him."

"But *why* is he that way?"

"I don't know, Amanda. He had everything to be thankful for, looks, brains, talent, money, position. Of course his mother neglected him. She never cared about anyone but herself, possibly a little for Thomas, but even her love for him was a selfish love. And she always played favorites, favored Thomas over your father when he was little. He was an odd little boy, very original and bright, but difficult, and Thomas was sweet and amenable, like Phoebe . . ."

"And I'm like Father," I added.

"Well, I hope to heaven, not *just* like, but there is a resemblance in temperament—yes. It must have hurt him that she seemed to love Thomas more than she did him. He told me once that, though he loved Thomas very much, he could never forgive the fact that Thomas was allowed to live at home while he was sent away to school when he was only twelve. He felt he was being got rid of because he was a problem. He joked about it when he told me but I know it hurt him. It's the closest thing to criticism I've ever heard him say about his mother."

That fall and winter Mother's attacks of asthma were more frequent and prolonged than they had ever been before, but sick or well she continued, as she always had, in the evenings to read aloud to us. Frequently overcome by fits of coughing and choking, she would be forced to pause to gasp for breath and to smoke her powder; we would beg her to give it up and go to bed, but as soon as she got her breath she would hurry on as if her life depended on it, stopping only as the hour grew late to ask: "Aren't you tired, girls?"

Phoebe, who took catnaps in between, always revived to echo my "No, no," until at last she would fall sound asleep, Mother and I exchanging fond amused glances at the sight of the rosy face that a moment ago had protested she wasn't "a bit sleepy."

One evening, reading *Les Miserables*, the subject of illegitimate children came up. Of course Rachel and I knew all about this because Mother had explained it when she had read us *Bleak House* during the winter at 12 Wellington Street, but Phoebe had been too young then to understand.

Now she read us the scene where little Cosette and Jean val Jean are on their way to the well on Christmas Eve and pass the shop with the magnificent doll. Suddenly Phoebe who had been dreaming on Mother's bed sat up and said: "But, Mother, who was Cosette's father?"

"Oh, Phoebe!" I groaned, but Mother put down her book and carefully explained.

When she had finished Phoebe said earnestly: "Do we know any illegitimate children?"

"No, of course not," I began impatiently, longing to get on with the story, but something in Mother's expression stopped me. "*Do* we?" I gasped.

To my surprise she did not say no, but sat deliberating for a moment, her cheeks and mouth sunk in her cupped hand, then she turned to us: "No, thank God, we do not!" she said, but there was a look in her eyes that made me wonder if perhaps we did.

As always, the evenings ended by Mother's telling us stories about her life. One story that seemed to haunt her that winter was the one about her first asthmatic attack.

". . . Father was terribly worried about me. I was only four or five years old. He had three nurses around the clock. He told me afterward that pneumonia had set in and he didn't expect me to live. One night when I was at my sickest, lying in my bed, I looked over and there sitting in my little rocking chair in the corner of the room was an old woman wrapped in a gray dressing gown rocking and rocking. I stared at her for a long time, fascinated but puzzled by her appearance; she didn't look like anyone I had ever seen, certainly not my own mother who was tall with a beautiful pink and white skin. This old woman was tiny and very gray . . . I never saw her again until after your birth, Amanda, when I was so ill, then the night I was at my lowest, the same old woman appeared in my room in her gray wrapper, rocking and rocking . . . It's a strange thing. She comes only when I am very ill . . . as if she were trying to tell me something . . . This winter she has been here twice. I never knew when I was young, who she was. It was always a mystery to me. Now I know! That old woman is myself!"

Another story that we heard more than once that winter

was the one about Aunt Belle, the night before her death, when Mother had been waked out of a sound sleep:

"I sat up in bed and there she was, my sister, Belle, as plain as I am to you, her face looking at me so earnestly and her clear voice saying 'Goodbye, Liza, I love you,'" and here Mother always broke down in the telling and wept, while we crowded round her chair to comfort her. Then she would continue, "Her face was as clear to me—I swear by everything that's holy—as if she were right in the room. Perhaps she was. Who but God knows the answer to such things? And when she had gone I happened to look at the clock on my dresser and it said three o'clock. Early the next morning my sister, Hildred, telephoned and said that Belle had died during the night. 'She died at three o'clock this morning, didn't she?' I said. 'Yes,' said Hildred 'exactly at three o'clock! My God, Liza, how did you know?'"

On one occasion when she was telling this story, I decided to take the bull by the horns and ask her something that had been puzzling me ever since the evening with Rupert at Pinky Whittemore's Hallowe'en party:

"Mother, what was the matter with Aunt Belle? Was she crazy?"

"Who *told* you that?" Mother was angry as I knew she would be. The gleam in her eyes and the sharpness to her voice told me that.

"Rupert did. He said she was bats in the belfry, didn't he, Phoebe?"

"That was a very wicked thing for Rupert to say and it's false, utterly *false!*" Mother said sternly. "Belle was *not* crazy, not by a long shot. She did have spells of melancholia as I've told you, but she was certainly *not* insane. If there's any bad blood anywhere it's not in *my* family."

MOTHER'S ILLNESS

Every Sunday, but no longer with Rachel to shepherd us, Phoebe and I went by streetcar to Sunday School at Christ Church, dressed in our best coats and our wide-brimmed black beaver felt hats with the long black streamers.

Although she never went to church herself, Mother had insisted from the time when we first lived in Cambridge that we go to Sunday School. To her, Christ Church was the finest church in Cambridge; I think she felt that apart from the religious education, our going there gave us a certain distinction that we would not otherwise have had.

Dr. Prescott Evarts, rector of Christ Church, was a thundering fire-and-brimstone preacher whose sermons might have been inspired by a revivalist fervor. After our regular Sunday School sessions we were always taken into the church whose beauty, the high-vaulted ceilings, dazzling white interior, magnificent stained-glass windows and deep red carpets, made more of an impression on us than we were aware of at the time. Here we would sit spellbound, not so much by the contents of Dr. Evarts' sermons as by his method of delivery.

Pounding the pulpit with one hand, he shouted out what sounded more like curses than blessings, while with the other hand he waved or pointed straight at us, his pincenez clinging precariously to his middle finger. I couldn't keep my eyes off those pince-nez as they flew around, behaving as if at any moment they would surely take off and crash onto the red carpet, but they never did.

Although the Sunday School teachers were young and pleasant, the classes were excessively dull with endless tracts in fine print about the splendid work being done in such and such a mission in Africa or China followed by short blurbs about the Good Samaritan or Joseph and his brethren. I got very little out of it except to wonder idly now and then why they went way over there to preach the gospel and provide clothes and shelter when there were so many poor people right in Cambridge.

That winter Phoebe and I fell into the reprehensible habit of neglecting to put the dime Mother gave us into the plate and using it instead to buy ice cream cones at Fiske's in Harvard Square. We also got into the habit that year of going almost every Sunday to the Georgian Cafeteria with the fifty cents Mother gave us for our Sunday dinner (always a half broiled chicken.) As the weeks wore on that winter we discovered why Mother was sending us so often.

So accustomed were we by now to her asthma that we had become almost callous, although we were vaguely aware of the gradual increase and severity of the attacks. "Nervous asthma," the doctors called it; according to them there was little to be done for it. She herself had given up hope of ever being cured. She had tried everything even to having her nose operated on, not once but twice, a part of the bone removed and the sinuses drained, a dreadfully painful procedure. (Mother was a stoic when it came to things like that; she always said that for her having babies was "like rolling off a log.") She had even considered having all her beautiful teeth removed at the suggestion of one doctor who claimed *they* might be the cause of her illness. Grandpa Evans had put a stop to that.

In the old days she had loved to dance, had taught us

children the minuet, the waltz, the polka. How well I remember her whirling gracefully around our small living room at Wellington Street. Now it made her short of breath to dance with us even for a few minutes. Nowadays too, much of her old dramatic spirit had dimmed, the once vibrant voice was a hoarse whisper, the blue fire in the eyes a dark smudge. She saw no one except Grandpa Evans, on his now infrequent visits, and Cousin Emma; she had given up going to Mrs. Larkin's for dinner. Even her trips to the Boston Safe Deposit & Trust Company were few and far between.

Night after night she sat up, hour after hour rocking and coughing and smoking her powder and gasping for breath. When the attacks grew more severe she would be so badly congested she could not eat or sleep and would have to stay in bed from sheer weakness; then she would send for old Dr. Danby who would come, sit by her bed, talk with her for a while and after a brief examination (we girls were always sent out of the room at this point) write out a prescription.

Roused from our semiapathy, we were sympathetic and eager to do whatever we could. Considering myself the boy of the family, I loved to be the one to dash off on my bicycle to Olive's Pharmacy in Porter Square. As I rode swiftly along on those cold black evenings I fancied myself my mother's knight errant, a blend of D'Artagnan, Robin Hood, and Jean val Jean.

Dr. Danby's prescriptions were always for the same thing, morphine, the drug my grandfather railed against so violently. Apparently it was the only thing that gave my mother any relief.

CHRISTMAS AT SACRAMENTO STREET

Rachel arrived in Cambridge on Christmas Eve to spend the last few days of her vacation with us. Phoebe and I were ecstatic to have her home again. After our baked bean supper we hung our stockings on the foot of Mother's brass bed, Phoebe and I pretending for everyone's benefit, including our own, that Santa Claus was on his way. The next morning there were the usual enchanting presents Rachel and my grandmother had prepared for us. That was the year Father sent us velveteen dresses, black for Rachel, green for Phoebe, purple for me, with a purple satin bosom and purple satin collar and cuffs.

"Most unsuitable for a child of thirteen—his secretary must have picked *that*," Mother remarked, but I was delighted with it.

Grandpa Evans was very ill with pneumonia so there was no question of our even being *invited* this year. After Sunday School we returned to Sacramento Street for our Christmas dinner in our own kitchenette.

Rachel was almost fifteen years old now and very grown up. She was doing up her hair, the long dark curls wound up in a French twist at the back of her head. That afternoon after dinner she and Mother had a long conversation about her future. A social service career was her plan, a splendid idea Mother thought, but she had chosen Vassar College instead of Radcliffe, which was a blow. All the Evans sisters had gone to Radcliffe.

Then Rachel announced that she had a beau, a young

man she had met at the Thanksgiving dance at Deering Academy, and that she wanted him to call on us before she left, on the next afternoon in fact. "If you think you're well enough to have a caller, Mother," she said shyly.

At the outset Mother was terribly upset by this disclosure, protesting that Rachel was too young, that it wasn't suitable for a girl not yet fifteen to have a young man to call, but something about the expression on Rachel's face must have made her change her mind.

"No, Rachel, I think I am wrong," she said suddenly, "and you are quite right to want the young man to meet us. Of course I shall be delighted to have him come."

He arrived promptly at three o'clock the next afternoon. A good-looking youth of eighteen, Edward Trumbull came from a small town in Maine and was in his freshman year at Hampton College in Wychmere, a coincidence that was a cementing factor in the youthful romance. Mother couldn't help liking Edward, who had charming manners. Whatever his private feelings may have been, he behaved as if living like this in one cramped, small room was the most natural thing in the world. Always a charming hostess, Mother served him tea and cookies and Phoebe and I needed no second urging to tell him all about ourselves, our school, our friends.

"Why don't you kids do your vaudeville act for Edward?" said Rachel after we had exhausted every subject of conversation. "These two have a song-and-dance routine, Edward. They're really professional. Would you like to see it?"

"Sure would," Edward smiled encouragingly.

Without more ado Phoebe and I rushed to the kitchenette to dress ourselves up, I with a pillow in my bosom and a bathtub brush for a fan, Phoebe who was considerably shorter than I, as a dapper little gentleman with a neat penciled-on mustache, a hat, and Mother's umbrella as cane, and to strut around our living room, Phoebe's arms clasped around my waist suggestively close to the bosom, the standard vaudeville position, singing:

> *When you're all alone any old night*
> *And you're feelin' out of tune*
> *Take up your hat, close up your flat,*
> *Get out and get under the moon (I mean it)*
> *Get out and get under the moon.*

Soon after that Edward rose and said he must go, and Mother nodded her approval at his not overstaying his first call. Because Rachel had planned to go to see Grandpa Evans later that evening before returning to boarding school, she could not guide Edward to the YMCA where he was spending the night; Mother was, therefore, explaining to him how to get there, when Phoebe, whose brown eyes had been fastened to his face for several minutes, piped up:

"I'll show you where it is, Mr. Trumbull."

"Do *you* know how to get there?" Edward asked surprised.

"Yes, of course," said Phoebe. "It's right next to the Boston Arena. I go skating there all the time. Maybe you'd like to go skating with me there. You can rent skates, you know."

"Why, what a good idea! I think I'd like very much to do that. If it's all right with you, Mrs. Willard?"

"Yes, yes, of course it's all right as long as you're back by supper time, Phoebe."

So Phoebe in her velveteen skating skirt, that Mother had made her, with her Scotch cap to match, took Edward by the hand and led him to Boston on the streetcar.

AUNT BELLE'S DEATH

That night after Rachel had returned from Westminster Avenue, long after Phoebe and I had gone to bed, she and Mother sat up in the kitchenette talking. She was to leave the next afternoon and they still had many things to settle. None of their conversation interested me enough to keep me awake until I heard Rachel saying:

"But *why?* Why did she *do* it?" Her voice was high pitched, distressed, as if she were going to cry. I sat up in bed and listened hard.

". . . something I don't like to talk about . . ." Mother was speaking now, "My poor sister—I don't think I can ever get over it . . ."

I sprang out of bed and over to the door of the kitchenette.

"What is it?" I said in a loud whisper.

Mother put her finger to her lips and gestured for me to shut the door.

"Mandy dear," she said softly, "It's very late and you need your sleep. Please go back to bed."

"That's not fair!" I was indignant. "When Rachel isn't here you tell me things and as soon as she gets home you leave me out. Please tell me. I'm old enough to know."

Mother hesitated, then glancing across the room at Rachel who sat staring at the kitchen table she said: "Cousin Rupert was at Grandpa's this evening while Rachel was there. He told her something. You tell her yourself, Rachel. She may as well know it now." Then looking at me earnestly, "You may as well know these things—if your Cousin Rupert is old enough I suppose you are—though why Bessie tells him so much I will never understand . . ."

"But Bessie *didn't* tell him," said Rachel. "He overheard something Grandpa and Uncle James were saying and he asked Bessie to explain it to him."

"What did he hear?" I said quickly.

"Well he stayed there one weekend last summer when his parents were away and he heard Uncle James and Grandpa talking one night about Aunt Belle."

"Yes?" I urged.

He heard them in the room next to him," Rachel continued, "they were having an argument—a quarrel really. Uncle James got very angry and said a lot of things in a very loud voice—most of them Rupert couldn't understand —but one thing he heard plainly was that Aunt Belle had no right to do what she did—that it was a sin! Then Grandpa grew upset and rang for Albert and Albert came and put him to bed and made Uncle James leave him."

"My poor father!" Mother said.

"That's what Rupert said. He said Uncle James is always railing against Grandpa for things," Rachel went on. "Anyway the next day Rupert went to Bessie and insisted that she tell him what the quarrel was all about and what sin Aunt Belle had committed. So Bessie told Rupert that Aunt Belle had not died a natural death—that she had killed herself! Oh I think it's so horrible!" and Rachel put her head in her hands and sobbed.

"But why?" I cried. "Why would anyone *do* such a thing?"

"I wish to heaven Bessie could keep her mouth shut!" exclaimed Mother. "She has no business telling Rupert these things—and he has no business telling you, no *busi-*

ness! I'm going to have a talk with his mother—and with Bessie . . ."

"Oh no, Mother, please don't!" cried Rachel splashing away her tears. "It's not Bessie's fault—Rupert sort of knew anyway—and so did I—I guessed something was wrong and I *made* him tell me—it wasn't his fault, really."

"Very well then," said Mother solemnly. "Since you know this much I suppose I must tell you the rest of it. You may as well know it from me as to hear a garbled version from someone else. Your Aunt Belle did kill herself. As I told you before, she had spells of melancholia, but she was *not* insane as *some* people have tried to say. Belle was desperately unhappy and bewildered and with good *reason:* she was going to have a child!"

"And she wasn't *married!*" cried Rachel.

"No, she wasn't married. The child would have had no father."

"An illegitimate child!" I exclaimed.

"Ssh," Mother shot a warning glance at the bedroom door. "Phoebe is too little to understand these things. Promise me you will say nothing to her until she is old enough to insist upon knowing, as you two have insisted, and then tell her—quietly and calmly as I am telling you now. Promise me that, both of you."

We solemnly promised.

". . . and you must not tell anyone else ever—you must not talk about it to *anyone,* Rupert or anyone else. Do you understand?"

We understood.

"Yes," she went on, "Poor Belle—she was almost five months pregnant when she decided to take her life—and nearly out of her mind with worry—but she was *not* crazy. Don't ever, *ever* let anyone tell you she was. There is no insanity in our family. Remember that! She talked with me for a long time the day before she died—apparently she had made up her mind then what she was going to do, though of course I didn't know it—and she was as sane as you or I. But she *was* crazy with grief and worry—and the miserable cur who was the cause of it—whom she'd been madly, senselessly in love with . . ."

"Who was it?" said Rachel. "Did you know him?"

Something—a grimness in Mother's expression made us both cry out together: "You did! You knew him!"

"Yes," she said. "I knew him."

"Who was it?" Rachel said quickly.

"I can't tell you that, girls. And *you* don't know him anyway," she added.

"But what was his *name?*" I insisted.

She got up and walked to the door of the bedroom, then turned dramatically. "He has no name," she said with that peculiar glitter to her eyes that always made me shiver. "He's a man without a name!"

JANUARY 2, 1967

The next day Rachel had to return to school. Every day during her visit Mother had got up and dressed and kept up her spirits for the holidays and for Rachel, but almost as soon as the door closed, she broke down and wept.

"What have I done? What have I done?" she said over and over.

We thought she meant letting Rachel leave us to go to

boarding school but it was more than that. When Rachel was at Grandpa Evans, that evening after Edward's call, Mother had gone to put a little surprise in Rachel's suitcase, her old gold watch on a chain that her mother had given her and that she hoped Rachel would prize. But to her dismay, when she opened the suitcase, she found six hats.

"Imagine bringing *six* hats on a five-day visit!"

"What's so terrible about that?" I said.

"You're too young to realize it, Amanda, but *I* know. This is a symbol, the handwriting on the wall—of what's to come! Physical! *Purely physical!* Just like her father—and his mother. *She's* the one who's responsible for this! It's her very *essence*. She cares for *nothing* but the physical. Things of the spirit mean nothing to her."

There was a great deal more of this but I found it impossible to pay attention. It struck me as absurd to worry about such a trifling matter as six hats; I knew my sister Rachel, and it didn't worry me at all. Mother's tirade seemed like the ravings of a mad woman. I couldn't bear to listen any more and went into the kitchenette leaving Phoebe in the living room with Mother. Presently Mother called me and reluctantly I returned.

"You think I'm foolish to worry about this, don't you, Mandy?"

"Yes, I do," I said staunchly; "I know Rachie and I know she's good. She's young and naturally all young people like pretty clothes. Didn't you like pretty clothes when you were young?"

"Well, you may be right," Mother said. "You may be right. I hope to heaven you are. What do you think, Phoebe? Do you think I'm foolish to worry?"

This surprised me that Mother should now be asking Phoebe's advice.

"Yes, I do. I *like* Rachel's hats," said Phoebe.

"Well, girls, you're probably right. I'm probably making too much of it," Mother rejoined.

Later that evening, however, she again began fretting, this time about Edward.

"That young man has a deathly pallor. I'm afraid—I'm very much afraid—he's not a strong person. In fact, I'm almost *positive*—of course I could be wrong—but I have a strong suspicion that he *may* be a consumptive!"

"Oh no!" I cried and Phoebe protested also, though she had no idea, and I little more, what a consumptive was. Mother was not to be argued out of *this*, however, and late into the night she talked about Edward's health.

"I am a doctor's daughter, Amanda, and I know the signs. That young man is a consumptive! I doubt very much if he lives to be twenty-five!"

It was my private thought that since she had been unable to find anything else wrong with him she had seized on his pallor as his only flaw, not because she objected to him as a person, but as a symbol of my grandmother's power. She turned to Phoebe for support.

"What do you think, Phoebe? You agree with me, don't you?"

"Ye-es," Phoebe said uncertainly, torn between her loyalties. I had kept my temper until now but at this I exploded.

"I don't believe it!" I spat.

"What do you mean?" There was an ominous ring in her voice.

"I don't think he has consumption at all. You're just trying to find something wrong with him. You're always doing that—trying to find something wrong with—"

"With whom, Amanda?" said Mother her eyes deep and sad gazing at me.

"With *everybody!*" Before the words were out I re-gretted them, but having started I couldn't stop. "You're always saying terrible things—about people. I think you're *mean!*" and bursting into wild weeping I stamped out of the bedroom, through the kitchenette, and down the hall to the bathroom.

The bathtub was still three-quarters full of gray soapy water. It was Saturday, the Flannagan's bath night. Sitting on the edge of the tub, only half aware of what I was doing, I bravely plunged my hand into the slimy stuff and unloosed the plug. Floods of tears flowed down my cheeks. I tried to think of something that Mother or someone had done to hurt *me* but I couldn't. Of course she had turned to Phoebe for support when I was usually the one—and Phoebe had agreed about Edward's being a consumptive to curry favor with Mother—but still—was that enough? Wasn't the truth really that *I* had hurt Mother? Could I be crying about that? What I had *not* said but really had meant, when she asked me, was that she was trying to find fault with my grandmother. More than my rudeness, it was this undercurrent of loyalty to my grandmother that had made her gaze at me so sadly. Of that I was sure.

I knew too that underlying all her talk about six hats and Edward's consumption and the bad influence of Grandmother Willard something more basic was troubling Mother: Rachel was growing away from us. I had noticed it myself.

When she had arrived home that first afternoon, looking so radiant in her soft brown coat with the beaver collar and the brown tam with the beaver pompoms, presents from my grandmother, her glowing immaculately clean person had contrasted sharply with Phoebe's and my own spotted jerseys, serge skirts, and soiled leather jackets. Later that day for old time's sake we had all three gone out for a few hops on the pungs, making their way down Oxford Street after their daily rounds, and Rachel had been as jolly and affectionate as ever with Phoebe and me, calling us "kids" and putting her arm around us, but there was a subtle difference in her manner. When we had returned to the house I had sensed that she was appalled at the narrow little room with the rumpled brass beds and the stuffy smoke-filled atmosphere. I had noticed too when we cleaned up for Edward's call that Rachel had scrubbed things Mother never bothered with: the stove, the tiny ice chest, even the floor here in the Flannagan's bathroom.

It was as if I suddenly saw our whole life with Rachel's eyes. She had been eager to show off her mother and sisters to Edward and Edward to us, but I knew the shabby poverty of the place must be more shocking now that she was no longer living here.

I had felt it myself when I had returned one morning after spending the night with a friend. As I entered the kitchenette, the meanness, the clutter, the pervasive smell of sickness mingled with the early morning smells of un-made beds and frying eggs had shocked and disgusted me; a wave of nausea had grasped me. For one moment I had felt that I wanted to get out as quickly as possible, out into the clean air, back to my friend's house, somewhere, any-where but here. Then another wave, of shame at my dis-loyalty, had swept over me.

So now as I sat in the Flannagan's bathroom staring miserably into the scum-rimmed bathtub, at the gray froth gulping its way down the drain, my mind floundering among the confusing welter of thoughts and feelings, there struggled to the surface a feeling stronger than the others —of deep pity for my mother.

Quickly I dried my tears and hurried back to our room to throw myself at her feet and ask her pardon. But the room was dark. Phoebe was asleep and Mother was in bed, her shoulders in the old gray wrapper hunched high on her pillows, her back to me, seemingly asleep too. It was unlike her to go to bed so early. It troubled me that I couldn't tell her I was sorry; she had said to me so many times, "Never let the sun go down on your anger, Amanda," but I could not disturb her, so I climbed into bed with Phoebe where I slept when Rachel was not at home.

The next day Mother was very ill. I had heard her get up several times in the night to sit in her chair and rock and smoke her powder and I knew she was worrying about things, but it was not until morning that I realized she was having another bad attack.

Her manner, moreover, was strangely removed, unlike her usual warm affectionate self, as if she were thousands of miles away. She seemed to have forgotten all about the talk of the evening before.

"Amanda," she said from her bed, "I'm not going to get up today." Her voice was a whisper, her eyes black with fatigue. "Take some money from my bag and after Sunday School you and Phoebe go to the Georgian Cafeteria for your lunch, will you, darlings? I'm going to get Dr. Danby here. I've had a very bad night."

"I'm sorry," I muttered. Again I wanted to throw my arms around her and apologize for last night's rudeness but something held me back, her detached manner perhaps, or my own stubbornness.

"Oh Mother, can't we stay home today?" begged Phoebe. "I don't *want* to go to Sunday School. Let me stay home and take care of you—*please.*"

"No, dearest, you go with Amanda. I'll be all right. I'd like to be by myself for a little while and rest," and she shut her eyes wearily.

So Phoebe and I went off on the streetcar, as we always did, and after Sunday School to the Georgian Cafeteria for our Sunday dinner but the broilers didn't taste good that day; they were raw and bloody at the joints. Phoebe and I couldn't finish them.

We returned to 113 Sacramento Street to find Dr.

Danby at Mother's bedside and as usual we were asked to go into the kitchenette while he talked with her. After he had gone Mother called to us to come in.

"Will one of my dear girls go to Olive's Drug Store and get this prescription filled?" she asked and Phoebe spoke up quickly.

"Let me, let me."

I felt deeply wounded that I wasn't to be the one to go until I realized that this would give me a chance to make my apology. Phoebe was just starting out of the door, however, when Cousin Emma appeared. Apparently Mother had telephoned her and asked her to come over so there was no chance for me to speak with her alone. When Phoebe returned and Mother had taken the medicine she summoned us to her bedside.

"Girls, I want to talk to you for a few minutes. Please sit here."

We drew up our chairs and listened attentively.

"I want my girls always to be fine, honorable, and kind with strength and character, not weak and sick like their old mother." We started to protest but she held up her hand and smiled fondly at us. "I know. You love me and that's what has kept me going all these years, my darlings, your love and the little courage I have."

"But you have a whole lot of courage, Mother," cried Phoebe.

"Yes, I have courage, but not enough, Phoebe dear, not enough." A fit of coughing overcame her and she had to stop to get her breath. "Now listen for just a moment more and then you must go in and play some quiet game in the kitchen and let me rest and Cousin Emma, good kind Cousin Emma, will stay and get us some supper, won't you Emma dear?"

"Of course I will, Lizby. I'm always glad to help."

I wasn't glad. I couldn't understand why Mother had

asked her to come when she knew we were perfectly capable of getting supper ourselves.

"I'm tired, dears, very tired these days. I don't know how much longer I can go on."

Again we started to protest and again she held up her hand.

"But you girls are young and strong and good. I've tried to bring you up to be that—and you have repaid my efforts a hundredfold. I couldn't ask for three better girls than my Rachel, and my Mandy," and she reached out and took my hand and pressed it in her thin white one, "and my little Phoebe," and she touched Phoebe's curls and patted her cheek and as she did this a pain shot through me, but only for a moment. She had told us this so often, and so often had said, as she was saying now, that she couldn't go on much longer that we simply bowed our heads and said nothing. "Now, dears, you go and play. I'll rest for a while," and she turned over in bed and, at a signal from Cousin Emma, we disappeared into the kitchenette and shut the door.

We must have been in there for an hour or more. Deeply absorbed in a game of Sir Hinkham, we had forgotten our worries about Mother and were laughing uproariously at some piece of foolishness, then remembering we were supposed to be quiet, stifling our guffaws with snorts and giggles which made us laugh all the harder, both of us for some reason strangely, wildly excited, almost hysterical, when suddenly the door to the kitchenette was flung open and Cousin Emma was screaming:

"Amanda! Girls! Come quick! Something has happened to your mother!" We dashed into the room to find Mother fallen from the side of the bed almost to the floor. "Help me get her up, Amanda!" Cousin Emma shrieked.

With superhuman effort she and I lifted the stiff and heavy body back onto the bed while Phoebe shrank back sobbing and frightened. Mother's face was blue and her large, high-bridged nose had been pushed to the side of her face by the fall. Her nose was one of Mother's few vanities.

I burst into tears and cried out, "Her nose is broken! Her nose is broken!" but Cousin Emma disregarded this and kept screaming, "Help me get her up! Help me get her up!"

The bewildered woman thought if she could get Mother to her feet and walk her around the room she could wear off the effects of the morphine. But this was impossible. Mother had had a stroke. The amount of morphine she had taken, in her asthmatic condition, was suffocating her. This in turn had affected her heart.

After that all was confusion. Cousin Emma rushed to the kitchen and distractedly started making coffee. Phoebe crouched helplessly in a corner of the room sobbing. I stood wringing my hands. What should I do? Grandpa Evans flashed through my mind. I ran downstairs. The Flannagans weren't there. I used their telephone anyway, but from Backbay 4425 a strange voice answered, the nurse who was attending Grandpa in his pneumonia. Bessie and Albert were out and the old doctor was too ill to speak to anyone. Under *no* circumstances was *anyone* to disturb him.

"But my mother!" I cried "She's—she's—someone's *got* to come right away!" Then I had an idea. "Is my Uncle James there?"

"Young Dr. Evans is not here," said the nurse. "He can be reached at the Peter Bent Brigham Hospital," and before I could stop her she had hung up.

My fingers clumsy and numb I searched through the telephone book and telephoned the hospital but the female voice at the other end was coldly indifferent. Dr. Evans was in the operating room. If I would leave the name and

telephone number he would return the call when he was
free. Too frantic to think to report that it was his own sister
who was stricken I hung up despairingly and then, when I
remembered and tried to call back, the operator's voice
kept insisting:

"I'm sorree—the liun is busy."

Then I called Dr. Danby. His wife answered. The doctor
was out of town. But she would telephone his assistant and
he would come as soon as possible.

"Don't worry, Miss Willard, I'll keep trying until I locate
a doctor who can go," she said kindly, and in the midst of
my frenzy I couldn't help a tremor of pride. I had never
been called "Miss Willard" before.

I hurried back upstairs to find Cousin Emma still fussing
with the useless coffee. Then within half an hour a strange
doctor arrived and Phoebe and I were dismissed from the
room. After he had gone we were told by Cousin Emma
that Mother had had a stroke but this meant nothing to us.
We were still unaware how critical was the situation.
Cousin Emma gave us some soup and we went to bed,
Phoebe downstairs with the Flannagans, who had been off
on a Sunday afternoon outing and had just returned, and I,
having insisted that I must stay with Mother, in the big bed
on the other side of the room. Cousin Emma was to spend
the night in a room down the hall from us and I was to call
her if need be.

The sight of that still figure on the bed, the face now
almost black, filled me with a sickening uneasiness but she
was breathing steadily and I assured myself that by tomorrow everything would be all right. The doctor had come.
Cousin Emma had told me before she went to her room
that he had given her an injection of something that should
"bring her round."

After I had knelt down and asked God to help my
mother, I threw myself on the bed and went sound asleep

for a couple of hours when abruptly I was awakened by a frightful sound from across the room. I had often heard Mother gasp for breath but this was different. It was as if heavy chains were being dragged across the room. I sprang out of bed and down the hall to Cousin Emma.

This time she took over. I was sent downstairs to the Flannagans so dazed I couldn't think. I was sure, positive, it *could* not be otherwise, that by morning, or in a few days perhaps, Mother would be all right. But underneath was another feeling, cold and heavy, which I dared not put in words. Cousin Emma summoned the doctor once more, Uncle James came and Aunt Hildred, but I knew nothing of this. All I knew was that in the morning when Phoebe and I went upstairs to our room Mother was no longer there. The bed had been stripped and on the mattress was a dark stain. It was the end of the world.

THE FUNERAL

Mother's body had been taken down and laid out in the front parlor of 113 Sacramento Street where Mr. Flannagan had his undertaking business. We had never been allowed to set foot in that parlor, but now for some reason, difficult for me to understand, I made my way again and again, stealing in to stand for long moments by the silent figure under the white sheet, the silver hair streaming from the noble forehead, the pale lips gently curved, almost smiling. I would stand gazing at this strange being, would reach out and touch her cold neck and face, fascinated, unable to believe that this was Mother.

On the third day when I crept in she was different. Her nose had been straightened, her cheeks and lips rouged, something she had never done in her lifetime, her hair marcelled. She was beautiful, but no longer anyone I had ever known.

The funeral was at the Mt. Auburn Cemetery. Rachel had been summoned from school. All the Evans family were there except Grandpa who was still too sick to go out. My father came. Grandmother Willard had sent word that she was not well enough to make the trip.

As we were driven through the bare streets that morning in the large hired limousine, I looked out at the city, my eyes bleared, my face stiff with weeping, unable to understand how the streetcars could still be rattling along their tracks, the people hurrying by as if nothing had happened.

There was a short service by a clergyman who had never known Mother. Then we were escorted up to the brass railing around the chancel to look at the body in the casket before it was taken to be cremated. This had been Mother's request. I remember Phoebe, who had not realized until this moment that Mother had gone from her forever, clinging to the brass rail, sobbing, no one able to persuade her to let go, until suddenly Father stepped forward, lifted her up by her elbows and swiftly carried her from the chapel. After that he left as quickly as he had come.

He was not present after the service at the family conclave outside the chapel. It was just the Evans family. What was to be done with Phoebe and me? Of course Rachel would live with my Grandmother Willard. That had been settled long before.

Uncle Freddy, Mother's younger brother, who lived out

west and whom we had never seen before, came forward and offered to take Phoebe; he and his wife had no children and would be glad to have her. There was an awkward silence.

Suddenly Aunt Hildred spoke up: "Your Uncle Rupert and I would be very glad to have you live with us, Amanda" she said.

"Oh no! no!" I cried and rushing to Phoebe's side threw my arms around her. We stood clinging to each other and crying:

"Please don't separate us! Please don't separate us!"

At this point Rachel took matters into her own hands.

"My grandmother is very sorry she can't be here," she said in a firm voice, "but she wants us *all* to go to Wychmere. She doesn't think we should be separated." I felt a sigh of relief go round the group.

My grandmother had said nothing of the kind, as we found out later, but Rachel spoke with such assurance that no one questioned her. So the matter was settled. To Maine we went the next day and with that move an entirely new chapter in our lives began.

It was January 5, 1927, Mother's forty-seventh birthday.

AUNT HILDRED

The night of the funeral we spent at Grandpa Evans' big gloomy house on Westminster Avenue where my Aunt Hildred, who had volunteered to spend the night so we would have some "family" nearby, did her best to lift us from our misery.

The "old doctor" was still in bed, too ill to do more than croak hoarsely "Ah, here are my little darlin's" when we were allowed after supper to go up to the second floor and peer at him beyond the nurse's starched bosom, as he lay in his huge mahogany bed looking as frail and yellow as the pages of an old newspaper, utterly unlike the ruddy Grandpa we were used to. He seemed not to know that his "Lizzie darlin'" had died for he did not mention her name, just looked over at Aunt Hildred as she was leading us from the room and said fondly, "Thank you, m'dear."

After that Aunt Hildred took us up another flight of stairs to the bedroom shared years ago by Mother and Aunt Belle when they were girls, where she dragged from the floor of a closet a large dusty box of pictures of the Evans family.

"See, girls, this is your Great Aunt Eliza, a wonderful woman. Look at those magnificent dark eyes. Your mother was very fond of her and she loved her little namesake. 'Liza's the brightest child I ever saw,' she always said. Your mother was a brilliant woman, girls. You know that, don't you? She could read before she was three years old and she talked at six months."

Accustomed to the Evans family's hyperbole we paid small attention to these encomiums nor did Aunt Eliza's dour old-fashioned face have any meaning for us, but of course we were polite and sat poring over the pictures while Aunt Hildred rattled off her anecdotes.

"That's your Great Grandfather Evans, a fine man, girls. They say he used to whip all seven of his sons every night before they went to bed. Now, here's Cousin Sarah Porter, a lovely girl they all said—her face was all right but her legs were like a piano's— Isn't it too bad?" and "Uncle Llewelyn—handsome isn't he in that uniform—he was an officer in the British Navy, girls, but his mother spoiled him—see his face, weak and dissipated. Never spoil your children, girls. I hate spoiled children, don't you?"

Phoebe picked up a cleaner, newer-looking photograph and held it out to her.

"Oh yes. Isn't he cunning? That's your Cousin Rupert when he was only three."

"I wish he were here," said Phoebe to be agreeable.

"So do I, Phoebe. Poor child off in that miserable boarding school. He just hates it. I've been writing and telling him to come right home if he doesn't like it. If you like something, *do* it, if you don't like it, don't do it. That's what I say. What do you think, girls?"

We were at a loss for an answer having been brought up by Mother, in theory at least, under her philosophy of "Their's not to reason why, their's not to make reply, their's but to do or die." Under ordinary circumstances Rachel and I would have loved a good argument on the point but neither of us had the heart for it tonight.

". . . and here's a picture of your Aunt Belle," snatching another stiff brown photograph from the muddled pile. ". . . taken in her bicycling costume—how she loved that rig —terribly expensive—all hand made—Father protested when he heard what it was to cost but Belle *would* have it and he gave in as he always did—Father was very indulgent with us children. She did look charming in it," and Aunt Hildred gazed raptly at the picture.

"She looks a little like you," I said, more to be polite than anything else, for glancing at Aunt Hildred I could see little resemblance between the sisters. The girl in the photograph was tall and a trifle plump with masses of fair hair flowing over her shoulders and large pensive eyes under her "fringe"; Aunt Hildred, who Mother had always said was the beauty of the family, was small and dark and very thin, with a rather severe face, thin hair pulled tightly back and small birdlike eyes covered with rimless spectacles. Everything about her in fact reminded me of a bird, twittering from one subject to another, quick and phrenetic in her talk and movements.

"Oh, no," she said, "I didn't look anything like Belle even as a girl. She looked more like your mother, only she was blonde—not exactly pretty but charming looking with brilliant blue eyes." Then holding out another photograph, "Here's another of Belle with her dearest friend, Bertha Reid. Your mother has told you about Bertha, hasn't she?"

"No, I don't think so," said Rachel.

Aunt Hildred removed her spectacles and rubbed the bridge of her nose.

"Bertha was a peach of a girl. Her family were very rich *and* distinguished—society people—she was Belle's roommate at Radcliffe. She was engaged to Uncle James."

"She was?" Rachel was being polite.

"Yes—she was"—Aunt Hildred looked solemn—"but she broke the engagement."

"Why?" I asked.

"After Belle's death—I supposed your mother had told you—yes, well it was a terrible blow for James—poor fellow, he's never gotten over it . . ."

"That wasn't a very kind thing for her to do, was it?" said Rachel.

"No, I suppose not, Rachel, but people in those days had very strict principles, most of them. Bertha's family did. They insisted that she break it off. I don't know that I blame them. They knew the whole story of course—Belle and Bertha were very intimate."

"I think that was a terrible thing for her to do," I declared.

"Mandy," said Aunt Hildred, "you cannot judge these things fairly unless you know the facts."

"But I do know them . . ." I began.

"No, you don't know them, not all."

"Why here's a picture of Father!" exclaimed Phoebe. "Grandmother Willard has one like this, doesn't she, Rachel?"

She examined it carefully and passed it to me. He must have been about twenty at the time, wearing a high turtle-necked sweater, his hair springing like Lord Byron's from his high forehead; the youthful face was in profile, deeply serious with the trace of a pout to the underlip.

"He was very handsome, wasn't he?" mused Rachel, who was looking over my shoulder.

"Yes, I suppose you would say so, but I for one *never* found him attractive. He was too sensual looking for my taste," Aunt Hildred said.

A flurry of resentment moved inside me at her words. Who was she to disparage Father's looks when Mother, who certainly was in a position to know, had always said he was "a very beautiful young man." It was the first time in my life I had ever felt any loyalty to my father. But Aunt Hildred had thrust his picture out of sight and was rummaging through the box.

"Now where in the world are those pictures of your mother? I know you children would love to see them. Oh here they are," and she pulled out from the bottom of the pile two pictures of Mother as a little girl. "Liza always hated this one." She held it out to us, a somber-faced child in a high-necked old-fashioned dress. "She made a terrible fuss because she didn't like the way her hair looked, and so Father let her have another picture taken that winter—he always gave in to Belle and Liza when they put up a fuss." She held out another picture of the same little girl in the same costume with the same somber expression, only that this time the hair had been crimped.

So we sat, we three girls, looking dutifully at each of the photographs while Aunt Hildred talked on, telling us stories of their youth many of which we'd heard many times before from Mother herself.

". . . we had such a happy childhood . . . none of us wanted to *leave* home. Father was such a jolly person, and your mother, girls, I wonder if you realize what a remarkable woman she was. So clever—more than that—brilliant! She could do anything! Did she ever tell you the time she won the skating prize? No? Well, you know what a beautiful waltzer she was? But of course she'd never done much skating. One day we were all skating on Jamaica Pond. There was to be, among other events, a waltz contest. Liza had never waltzed on skates in her life. You know it's not easy. To be sure her partner was a good waltzer but even so it was remarkable. They won the first prize. I remember how lovely she looked that day in her green velvet skating costume with the sealskin cap and muff Father had given her for her birthday. It was just about this time of year. I suppose she was about twenty at the time." Aunt Hildred sighed. "She was so gay in those days, so full of high spirits, always thinking of wonderful things for us all to do—charades, impromptu skits, picnics, dances. Belle was the wit of the family, but Liza was the one who started everything. She marshaled us all around, even the boys did just what she said—and we all loved it too!" Aunt Hildred sighed again and shook her head. "If *only* she hadn't married Archibald Willard! But there's no use talking about that. Just remember, girls, when you think back on her that your mother was one of the brightest, prettiest, gayest people I've ever known. Everyone wanted to be where Liza was!"

But it was no use. Kind as it was of Aunt Hildred to say all these nice things about Mother I couldn't listen any more and the cardboard little girl, crimped or straight, held no comfort for us. She was a stranger.

PART FIVE

Wychmere

ARRIVAL

THE NEXT DAY we arrived at Wychmere in time for supper. Rachel had sent a telegram from Grandpa's house and Uncle Luke was at the station to meet us and to drive us up snow-covered Main Street to Pinewood, where we were greeted at the door by my grandmother herself.

She presented a charming picture standing there in her white wool dress with the black velvet ribbon she always wore high around her neck, "I hate old necks," she used to say, her white hair glistening under the light in the spacious front hall. I knew she liked herself that way because there was a photograph of her framed in gold in exactly that costume and pose in her upstairs sitting room.

"Welcome to Pinewood, girls," she said clearing her throat, which she always had to do before she spoke, and putting out her hands to Rachel and Phoebe and me (Uncle Luke had driven with our bags to the back door).

The contrast to 113 Sacramento Street was dramatic. It was impossible not to enjoy the palatial living room, the glorious fire in the black-bricked fireplace and the delectable aroma floating from the kitchen to assure us that supper was on its way.

The household was there to greet us, take off our coats and hats, kiss our cheeks, and smooth our hair. None of them spoke about Mother or the funeral or anything of the sort, but plied us with questions about our trip to which

213

Phoebe responded spontaneously and I, after the first moments of shyness had worn off, followed suit. Everyone chuckled at everything we said and I caught myself laughing aloud with gratification before I remembered that this shouldn't happen. How could I forget even for a moment Mother's still body under the white sheet?

As the evening progressed and everyone continued to make as much of the "little girls" as possible, it became increasingly evident that Phoebe was far and away the favorite. Rachel of course being well established as my grandmother's own child did not enter into the rivalry. That they had every intention of being impartial I knew, nor could I blame them for admiring Phoebe.

"Isn't she cunning?" "Just look at those dimples!" "Did you hear that, Luke?" was heard on all sides. During supper, served in the candlelit dining room, Minna and her daughter, Alma, who came in on special occasions to "give a hand," as they moved through the swinging doors from dining room to kitchen, laughed boisterously at everything Phoebe said. "Why don't they call it chicken à la queen? Ladies like it too" and so on, uttered with wide-eyed innocence, remarks that Phoebe would never have considered making had she been with me alone.

Such had been Mother's skill that each of us in her own way had felt herself to be Mother's special child. Phoebe was her darling baby, Rachel her chief support, I was the comical one, the odd one, the changeling. Mother had built me up, moreover, to believe I had a quality of genius. "She could go on the stage—look at the way she moves!" or "Amanda, can you say it that way—*just* like that!" when I was practising my Memorial Day address, a poem by Edgar Guest, to be delivered before the entire Agassiz School up on the platform with the Civil War veterans, shaky, faintly smelly, sweet old men who smiled at me or wiped away a tear when I pinned a carnation to their lapels.

As the evening wore on my mood darkened. Each time Phoebe was praised or laughed at I felt such a stab of pain that finally I could bear it no longer and stole into the darkened vestibule where I stood in a chilly corner among the wraps and furs, vaguely conscious of the aroma of moth balls, allowing streams of anguish to wash over me at the thought of Mother lost to me forever.

But it was not only when I felt myself ignored or ill treated that I was to suffer from the loss of my mother. For weeks, months, years she was to come unbidden into my thoughts sleeping or waking. The nights were the worst— the dreams. She was alive! I had found her in some remote spot, usually a nunnery. She couldn't return with me to 113 Sacramento Street, but she was going to arrange everything so we could all be together again. But I mustn't tell *anyone* that she was alive. That would break the spell. Then she would smile her sad smile, and before I could put out a hand to stop her she was gone and I was half awake angrily, silently shouting:

"She *is* alive! She *is* alive! She doesn't lie. Never! Never!"

She is with me still—her gray-blue eyes studying my face, one eyebrow cocked quizzically, one leg tucked under her, her graceful arm resting on the arm of her rocking chair, her fingers tapping out the words:

"Amanda, I want you to *promise* me something— something *my* mother used to say to me so often—*never* let the sun go down on your anger. Never *forget* these words, my dearest girl."

Of her many dictums this was to haunt me the most. I had not apologized to her in time and the sun *had* gone down forever. As I look back on it now my feeling for my mother was as intense as a love affair, so much so that no love affair since has been as meaningful.

After supper that night we gathered around my grand-mother at the piano and sang, as we had been accustomed to doing in past summer visits at Pinewood. Although she played with great élan, according to my sisters she was far from expert; but to me who was not as musical, it was a marvel to see anyone read music so fast, her gnarled be-ringed fingers moving rapidly over the keys ending up with a trill and a flourish of the hand. I sang the melody, Rachel the alto, and Phoebe, especially gifted in this way, could put a harmony to almost anything. I loved the old ballads, English, Scotch, and Irish that she played and the Gilbert and Sullivan operas. Tonight it was hymns. When we came to "Onward Christian Soldiers" my grandmother made a face and flicked over the page.

"I never could *abide* that," she said sourly.

Phoebe and I one on each side of her exchanged a tremor. It was Mother's favorite hymn. She had played and sung it with spirit in the old days before our piano had been put in storage. Rachel, standing behind my grand-mother turning the pages for her, stretched out a slim brown hand and flipped back the page.

"Please play it, Vicky," she said firmly. "*I* like it."

"Rachel, you do have the most *peculiar* taste some-times," Vicky grunted, but she played it, all six verses, with the twisted smile hovering on her lips throughout. Rachel sang them all, but although Phoebe and I tried our hardest, with Rachel smiling encouragingly at us, our voices quav-ered and broke and after the hymn was finished, we were glad to bid everyone good night and creep upstairs.

Rachel came up with us to show us around and soon after that Vicky followed.

"Have you said your prayers, girls?" she asked standing in the doorway clearing the frog from her throat.

We assured her that we had, whereupon she came in, gave us each a quick peck on the cheek, said kindly,

"Tomorrow we'll have another bed brought down from the attic and you may join Rachel on the sleeping porch," turned off the light, bade us good night, and shut the door.

That feeling of well being that always accompanied me on my visits to Pinewood crept over me as I lay between the clean smooth sheets, but my insides felt sore as if someone had pounded them for a long time. Then in the darkness beside me I heard Phoebe weeping softly. I had cried so much during the past five days I thought I could never cry again but at this sad little noise I too began to weep uncontrollably and in a moment Phoebe crept into bed with me, put her arms around me and we sobbed together until at last we slept.

LIFE AT PINEWOOD

The next morning I woke early. The room was filled with sunshine glancing off the snow-covered pine branches outside the nursery window, reaching its long winter-pale fingers across the foot of my bed. For a moment I wondered where I was. Then it came to me in a rush from my well of misery deep down, always there under everything I thought or felt. She was gone forever.

But this morning weakly filtering through my grief was a sense of joyful wonder that I, Amanda Evans Willard, was to live *here* in this unbelievably beautiful place. I glanced at Phoebe. She was still sleeping soundly, lying flat on her back, her mouth open, snoring slightly (she had inherited the Evans family's bronchitis), a beguiling picture even in this pose, with her dark gold hair tangled on the pillow, her cherubic face framed by the ruffled collar of her white flannel nightgown. I wanted to wake her but something about the sound of her snore, almost a sigh, plaintive and touching, prevented me. Putting on my bathrobe and slippers I moved carefully from the room, along the upstairs hall and down the wide front staircase to the landing.

Here on the walls were two enormous oil paintings of Father and Uncle Thomas as five-year-olds, idealized portraits in Lord Fauntleroy costumes with long yellow curls, Father standing with a wooden sword in his hand, in black velvet with lace collar and knee breeches, Uncle Thomas in velvet jacket and plaid kilt. I stood gazing at them. What if I might step into the heavy gold frames and join these beautiful children in their life of long ago? What kind of people would they be? Were they as charming as they looked? What kind of life had been theirs here at Pinewood? Everything in the past seemed so much happier, so much more romantic . . .

At the foot of the staircase I paused again. Once more the sense of wonder touched me, that this magnificent room stretching before my eyes, so different from our room at 113 Sacramento Street, so like something in a novel, was to be *my* home!

Very softly on tiptoe I wound my way around the living room examining everything, the huge antimacassared sofa and armchairs, the grand piano, the Medici prints lining the walls.

To me, the three most fascinating objects in the room were a heroic-sized marble bust of the Apollo Belvedere presiding on its stand at the bottom of the stairs; a bronze statue, not quite life-sized, entitled "Farewell to the Swal-

lows," of a nude maiden with her arms outstretched expos-
ing sharply pointed breasts upraised to the birds nestled
among her tresses, and a large oil painting of a plump
naked little boy, his head coyly peeping from behind an
arras, the lower part of his body, particularly his genitals,
ill concealed by the bunch of grapes in his chubby fist.

These masterpieces, bought by my Grandfather Willard,
who fancied himself a connoisseur of the arts, during his
sojourns in France and Italy, were to prove a source of
excruciating embarrassment to Phoebe and me on one occasion that winter, when two callow youths from the
Wychmere Grammar School came to play cards with us.
The loathsome little boy and the nubile maiden provoked
such snickers from them that Phoebe and I were forced to
confine our card playing and our cocoa drinking to the
kitchen, much to my grandmother's disapproval.

"You are *not* the cook and the second maid and I don't
care to have you behave as if you were. Entertaining your
guests in the kitchen indeed!"

Now, after a thorough examination, to the point of
gingerly touching the bronze maiden's nipples and scrutinizing the young man's lower parts with a magnifying
glass lying conveniently on a table nearby, I made my way
to the dining room. Here I stood and gazed solemnly
around me.

As in the nursery above, the thin winter sun was sifting
in, dancing on the sideboard laden with an elaborately em-
bossed coffee urn and massive candlesticks. Wandering to
the big window I gazed out at the snow-burdened wood.
How beautiful it all was! How Mother would have loved it!
Sighing deeply I turned away. Why couldn't we have been
all together in this lovely place? Why couldn't "they" have
managed it somehow? It all seemed so useless, my mother's
suffering, her hatred for my grandmother—and my father . . .

My thoughts trailed off when I thought of my father into something vague, ill defined. I felt confused. I didn't want to think any more. I passed on through the swinging doors into the butler's pantry where the sound of voices stopped me. Aunt Freida and Uncle Luke were in the kitchen having breakfast.

"Good morning."

It was Aunt Frieda's voice. Pretending not to hear I had already turned, paced swiftly back through the swinging door, around the big L and up the front stairs. I wasn't exactly afraid of Aunt Frieda, but she was not a person to be trifled with.

As I reached the second floor I heard my grandmother calling in her hoarse voice:

"Is that you, Rachel?"

"No'm—it's me, Amanda," I said, meekly approaching the door of her bedroom.

"Is it me or is it I?" She was sitting up in bed, dressed in her lavender challis bed jacket, her yellow-white hair in a neat pigtail down her back, a pink straw tray with legs straddling her lap. She always had her breakfast in bed.

"It's I," I said.

"Good morning. I hope you slept well."

The words were kind enough but I felt she was inspecting me. I was suddenly painfully conscious of my uncombed hair and my rather soiled blue wrapper whose top button dangled by a single thread.

"Oh, yes I did," I mumbled folding my arms tightly across my chest and stepping back out of her line of vision.

What luxury—to sleep in this lovely room and have someone bring that nice-looking breakfast up on a tray. The coffee smelled delicious. Mother often used to let me have a cup with her on weekend mornings when we sat chatting together, but I knew better than to expect the same of Vicky.

Yet I had to admit to myself that she had some sterling qualities. In spite of the breakfast in bed and the sporadic attacks of illness, she was an exceedingly industrious, rigidly disciplined person. Unlike Mother's, her household ran like clockwork, the daily routine strictly adhered to. Every morning after breakfast, as soon as she was neatly dressed in her "morning" dress, she set to work mopping and dusting the upstairs and polishing the porcelain in her bathroom. She was dreadfully fussy about her bathroom which she now had to share with Phoebe and me as well as Rachel. One face cloth, one toothbrush out of place was enough to cause a commotion; if one were careless enough to neglect to scrub out the tub after bathing or to rinse out the basin after brushing one's teeth or to leave hair in one's comb or brush one could expect a real scene.

Every morning when the weather was fine, after she had finished her chores and had conferred with Minna about the day's menu, she walked "down street" to Wychmere center a mile and a half and back to do her errands. First she would go to Hazelton's Market to pick out special delicacies, then to the bank, often to Baker's Dry Goods Store for elastic, ribbon, buttons, hooks and eyes or snaps, always to Simpson's Book Store for stationery or greeting cards or a book from the circulating library.

My grandmother, like my mother, was an insatiable reader. She too was to spend many hours reading aloud to us during the years to come, especially when we were sick with measles and scarlet fever. Dickens, Scott, and Charles Reade were among her favorites. I remember particularly while reading us *The Cloister and the Hearth* her hearty, rather hoarse laughter whenever she came to the often repeated phrase: "Courage, Camarade, le diable est mort!"

Dinner was always served in the middle of the day at Pinewood, at one o'clock sharp. After that my grandmother took her rest on her chaise longue for exactly one hour. She would then get out her workbasket and set to work mending. No loose button, frayed sleeve, or hanging hemline ever escaped her eye, exactly opposite to Mother, who loved to "run up" things in a hurry but hated the fussiness of mending.

Almost everywhere one looked at Pinewood one could see my grandmother's handiwork. In the side hall were shoe bags neatly nailed to the wall with places for each member of the family for overshoes, gloves, caps; in the bathrooms rows of hot water bottles; in the bedroom closets shoe cases marked in chain stitching "Rachel's Evening Slippers," "Victoria's Black Pumps," in her sewing table small bags labeled "Buttons," "Snaps," "Odd and Ends."

At four o'clock she rose from her chaise longue and changed into her afternoon dress, then went downstairs to receive callers or be driven somewhere in her automobile. Supper was always at six and after that piano playing and singing unless there was company, an occasional concert or play at Hampton College or the moving pictures. Vicky loved to give informal supper parties for her family and close friends; the chief entertainment after supper was usually several rounds of charades. Phoebe and I loved nothing better than to get up and perform, and like Mother, my grandmother found us highly amusing. Sometimes she laughed so hard at Phoebe she cried but with me she was apt to say sharply: "Amanda Willard, you are nothing but a clown—you'll do *anything* for a laugh!"

Vicky had had even less formal education than her older sisters. At fifteen when her father died suddenly leaving her mother with five children and no money she had had to leave school and go to work (an unheard of situation for a young girl of breeding in those days) as secretary to a lawyer friend of her father's, taking dictation and writing his letters in longhand. But because of her wide reading, and her life abroad with her husband, she was by no means uncultivated; indeed she was regarded as an intellectual in Wychmere, doubtless because she preferred the company of the faculty members of Hampton College to the townspeople. These, especially the females of her own age, she was apt to scorn: "I despise old ladies," she used to say.

At one stage in her career she had inspired a fond passion in the breast of one of the presidents of the college, a handsome man with a "melting" tenor voice, who used to spend several evenings a week at Pinewood, singing sentimental ballads to her piano accompaniment. We had heard about this romance from Mother: "Imagine carrying on with the president of Hampton College right under the nose of his wife! No wonder your father is the way he is with a mother like that!"

In spite of the regularity, luxury, and simple diversions of her existence, my grandmother was not a happy woman. Rachel and Phoebe and I could sense this. More than once I caught her unawares lying on her chaise longue gazing out of the window, a petulant, discontented expression on her mouth, a deep sadness in her eyes, as if life no longer had anything to offer her.

Now as I stood regarding her, so comfortable in her bed, sipping her coffee and freshly squeezed orange juice and nibbling her crisp toast, marmalade, and bacon, I felt a touch of resentment. I'll never, never be able to please this woman, I thought gloomily, never know how to get along with her. For one thing I never knew what she was thinking, except when she was angry. Like the tight corset she always wore binding the folds of her soft white flesh, Vicky's reserve bound her thoughts and feelings.

"Have you had breakfast, child?"

Her tart tone broke into my reverie. My heart lifted slightly at being called "child." This was as close as she ever came to being affectionate with me. Even toward Rachel, whom she considered her own child, she never displayed affection, never kissed her or hugged her or patted her hand the way Mother had with all of us. Only occasionally to Phoebe, who was more outgoing and less critical than her older sisters, Vicky showed her fondness by reaching out and pinching her cheek.

I looked up to find the brown eyes behind the pince-nez scrutinizing me carefully.

"No'm," I replied. "The others aren't up yet."

On the wall behind her bed was a picture of Uncle Thomas as a baby, a charming pastel of his head with its cap of gold curls against a background of soft blue.

"I love that picture of Uncle Thomas," I ventured. Here was a piece of ground I felt sure of. Vicky was very sentimental about her younger son, always wore his Alpha Delta Phi fraternity pin on her bosom and carried a locket with his picture and his baby hair.

"Yes, it's my most prized possession," she replied, sighing heavily. "Now, Amanda, it's time for Phoebe and Rachel to get up." The tone was suddenly crisp. Obviously *she* didn't want to chat. "I can't ask Minna to serve breakfast after eight o'clock with all she has to do. You realize of course she has a big load *now*, don't you?"

I nodded and hung my head.

"Well, run along then and wake them." She turned back to her breakfast. Then as I was about to go, "And oh, Amanda, everyone here at Pinewood *dresses* before going downstairs."

"Yes'm," I said and hurried from the room.

We three girls were dressed and downstairs for breakfast by eight o'clock. My grandmother never allowed us to sleep late even on weekends, Minna had too much to do to serve breakfast to stragglers, nor were we allowed to eat in or even set foot into Minna's kitchen during the meal because it "fussed" her too much.

Minna Buffum was as important a person in my grandmother's household as Bridget had once been in ours. A large woman with a battered face and untidy hair scraped into a bun at the back of her head, she was a native of South Barnstable, a little town near Wychmere. Never in her sixty-two years had she been farther North than Camden or farther South than Yarmouth. She spoke in a loud twanging voice with a down east accent, her communications usually in the form of complaints.

"Mis' Willard, I don' know what in the lands I'm goin' to do about them sausages—they're tainted again—this is the fo-uth time they've ben that way in a fo'tnight," or "I couldn't git them fish cakes to fry up proper no matter what I done to 'em; that codfish was froze as solid—it must of ben caught back durin' the Civil Wo-uh."

In spite of her querulous manner Minna was a kind-hearted woman. My grandmother depended on her to keep her household running as perfectly as it did and, without realizing it, we girls came to depend on her too, for the atmosphere she created. There was always a delightful aroma of baking ginger cookies or home-made bread or stewing fruit for jams or jellies issuing from the kitchen when we came in after school.

She came now shuffling into the dining room in her big shoes with the sides cut out for her enormous corns and bunions.

"He-ah, Rachel, you always git what you want, don't ya?" and she tossed a large plate of muffins on the table in front of my sister. "I should of thot what with fried bread you'd of had enough without me havin' to bake these."

"Oh, Midgie, you are a dear good thing," cried Rachel, pulling Minna's head down and hugging her. One side of Minna's shapeless mouth turned up in a grin, a dark red flushing her gray face.

"Oh stop that, you and your dears and goods," she said brusquely and slapped out again.

"She seems kind of cross," Phoebe whispered.

"Not really," Rachel whispered back. "That's just her manner. You'll see. Now, kids, we're going to have a wonderful day today. Edward called and he's coming over this morning to take us all tobogganning. The river is frozen over and just wait 'til you see the toboggan slides! There are two of them. You'll absolutely love it—both of you!"

"Will Vicky mind if we go?" I asked in a low voice.

"Oh no, not if I tell her I think it would be good for you. She usually takes my advice about things, especially about you kids. Vicky's all right when you get to know her and she *does* want to do the right thing for you two. She'll make us do some dusting and stuff and she'll fuss a lot but it doesn't mean anything. She's just bored. She'd probably like to come tobogganning herself. Just say 'yes'm' to everything and do a tiny bit of dusting and then we'll go! So let's hurry. Okay?" Her enthusiasm was catching. Phoebe and I brightened. We had never been tobogganning.

After breakfast my grandmother called us to her sitting room, where in a pale lavender morning dress she was busy dusting.

"I hope you enjoyed your breakfast," she said putting down her dust cloth and looking us over carefully.

"Yes'm," replied Rachel promptly.

"Yes'm," Phoebe and I echoed.

"Very well. Now, if you please, I should like to have a short talk with you for a moment. Please sit down."

Rachel threw us a reassuring glance and we disposed ourselves about the sitting room, Vicky in a straight-backed chair by her desk. These "short talks" in my grandmother's sitting room were to be a frequent occurrence at Pinewood, just as our conferences around Mother's rocking chair had been in the Cambridge days. Vicky cleared her throat.

"I'm very happy to have you girls all here together," A pause—something was obviously expected.

Phoebe spoke up, "We're very happy to be here, Vicky." I nodded solemnly.

"Rachel has always been contented and happy here at Pinewood, haven't you, Rachel?"

"Yes'm." Among the many rules laid down for us at Pinewood one was paramount. *Never* address your elders without a title.

"I think you will enjoy being here as much as she has," Vicky continued. "We shall all certainly do as much as we can to help you through this difficult time." A little sound from Pheobe, Vicky hurried on, "Rachel and I have talked it over and we have decided to leave it up to you as to whether you would like to start Monday morning here at the Wychmere Grammar School or whether you would like to stay home for a little while for the next week or two."

Rachel spoke up quickly, "I have to go back to Deering on Monday but I'll be here every weekend."

"I'd like to go to school if Mandy would," said Phoebe looking over at me.

"Very well, Phoebe, but you must learn to be independent you know, now that you are almost twelve. What about you, Amanda?" Her tone held more asperity as she looked in my direction.

"I'd like to go," I replied hastily. The thought of Pinewood every day without Rachel's presence was not an appealing one.

"Very well then. That's settled and I think you've made a wise decision. It's best at times like this to keep busy. Now what about church? Your sister does not go to Sunday School. She's of the opinion and so am I that she's too old for that but she does attend the Congregational Church with me every Sunday and she sings in the choir. I know you have been going to an Episcopal Sunday School and your Aunt Frieda goes to St. Anne's here in Wychmere. I don't care for the rector myself—his sermons are not at all to my taste—and intolerably long—but you are welcome to go there if you choose."

There was no hesitation about this. No matter what the sermons the thought of accompanying Aunt Frieda Appleton was enough to discourage us from St. Anne's, although we knew Mother would have preferred it for us. To the Congregational Church we would go therefore the next morning and sing with Rachel in the choir.

"Now, girls," said my grandmother clearing her throat again, "as you know, I am very particular, so I should like to have your things kept tidy, if you please, and on Saturday mornings I shall ask you to mop, dust, and carpet sweep your room. Of course, on weekdays you will have school and on Sundays we observe the Sabbath so it will only be one day a week. I don't think that's too much to ask. Alma is far too busy and of course I never ask Minna to do any cleaning—her feet are much too painful. So will you do that, please?"

"Yes'm, of course," we chimed eagerly.

"Now—as to your clothes," she continued, pursing her lips, "you will need things for church tomorrow and for school the next day . . ."

"Oh, we have plenty of clothes," blithely from Phoebe. "We just got new dresses from Father for Christmas."

"You may have plenty of clothes but what condition they are in is another matter. Please lay out any things that have spots or tears. I'm sure you'll find a considerable number that do—if not all," she added half under her breath, an expression of ill-concealed disgust on her mouth as she stood up to resume her dusting.

"Yes'm," Phoebe said meekly, and down the corridor to our bedroom we filed in silence.

Once inside the shelter of our room I turned to Phoebe.

"How can she talk like that—so soon?" and we both burst into tears. Quickly, softly, the door opened. Rachel stole into the room and put her arms around us.

"It's all right, kids. She doesn't mean it. Honestly she doesn't. She just can't help herself. Her bark is much worse than her bite."

We stood in a little knot by the window whispering so Vicky's sharp ears couldn't hear.

"But she's so mean!" I sobbed.

"I know. She *is* mean at times but she has her good side too . . ."

"I don't see *anything* good," I burst out angrily. "No wonder Mother couldn't bear her!"

"Mandy, dear," Rachel said gently, "you must realize— there *are* two sides to it. Vicky had a lot to bear too . . ."

"What?" cried Phoebe indignantly. "What did *she* have to bear?"

"Ssh!" Rachel put a finger to her lips. "I don't want to say anything against Mother—I loved her just as much as you did . . ." She stopped, her voice thick with tears, "But she was, you *know* she was, frightfully jealous of Vicky—and after all Vicky had warned her, *begged* her in fact, I know this from Vicky herself—it's one of the few things she *has* told me—*not* to marry Father. I think *this* was the thing Mother couldn't forgive more than anything else that Vicky had told her she *must not* marry him . . ."

"Why?" whispered Phoebe.

"Oh poor Father—I don't think he should have married anyone . . . But we mustn't let these things ruin *our* lives." Rachel's intelligent brown eyes regarded us earnestly, imploring us to be happy. "Come on. Let's cheer up. We're going to have a wonderful life here all together. It'll be so much fun. You've no idea. Wychmere is a great place!"

EDWARD

Edward arrived in his Chevy touring car, by careful pre-arrangement with Rachel, exactly as soon as we had completed our chores, and in a matter of seconds we had bundled ourselves into our leather jackets, French berets, and black buckled overshoes, left unbuckled of course except in my grandmother's presence. Like Mother, she considered "flappers" vulgar.

Leather jackets and French berets were very much in vogue that year. My jacket of green suede, bought for me by Mother at Jays in Boston, a real extravagance, was my proudest possession.

Now buttoning it up the front, I noticed a splash of grease across the left breast pocket. Spots on my clothes had never made the slightest difference to me when I lived in Cambridge, but now a feeling came over me that overwhelmed me, far more powerful than mere shame at my spots—I could have borne that—a feeling so deep and secret that I could not possibly have told anyone about it, not even Phoebe who had spots on her clothes too. When I was able to put it into words, I realized this feeling was one of inadequacy, more than that, of inferiority, something entirely new in my experience. Always before I had been so blithely confident that I could tackle whatever life handed out to me. But now this feeling, insidious and corrosive, was to be with me wherever I went, just over my shoulder, nagging at me, reminding me that something about me—I wasn't sure what—was wrong.

As I stood at the side entryway at Pinewood carefully arranging my scarf across my chest to hide the spot, I was tempted to give up the whole expedition, tear off the green jacket and rush upstairs to my bedroom to bury myself and my grief in my pillow, as I had so often done in the Cambridge days when things went wrong.

"Hey there, Mandy, what you doin'?"

Edward stood beside me, his black hair ruffled by the wind, his pale cheeks rosy, his blue eyes twinkling at me.

"Come on, kid!"

Before I could answer he had grabbed my hand in his leather paw and was pulling me across the icy yard to the Chevy, where Rachel and Phoebe were waiting.

"Hop in, honey," he ordered.

We drove off in the sweet, frigid air in the open car, Edward and Rachel in front, Phoebe and I in back with the toboggan, my heart swelling with pleasure. No man had ever before called me "honey."

As we rode along the glittering white breadth of Main Street toward the center of Wychmere and the river, I studied Edward's darkly handsome profile as he turned now and then to murmur something to Rachel or to toss back an encouraging quip to Phoebe or me. He looks very like Rudolph Valentino, I thought, with his gray fedora stylishly turned down in back, his perfect even teeth, narrow smile, and beguiling dimple.

But my feeling for him was not the agonizing longing I had felt for Rudy. To be passionately in love, as I had, with someone like Rudolph Valentino, whom one doesn't even know, seemed ludicrous to me even then, but as I look back on it my childish feelings for the beautiful Rudolph and later, in my adolescence, for the debonair Maurice Chevalier were my preparation for years of suffering for flesh-and-blood men who were often for me exactly as shadowy and two dimensional as the shining figures on the silver screen.

But Edward was different. Rachel had always been a bulwark for Phoebe and me and now, with Edward at her side, they assumed the role of parents for us. From that snowy morning when he seized my hand and pulled me from my dark mood, through the years at Pinewood, for me —and for Phoebe too—who had never had a brother or even a father, Edward was to be both.

THE SLEEPING PORCH

On the second floor of Pinewood leading from the nursery, so-called because it had been that for Father and Uncle Thomas and for Rachel, was the sleeping porch.

It was considered healthful in those days to sleep out-of-doors no matter what the temperature, so the day after our arrival my grandmother had a third bed brought down from the attic and set up alongside the two already there. Each of these beds was fixed with a circular frame on a supporting pole rising several feet above the bed; from the frame were hung Turkey red curtains which in cold weather could be pulled entirely around the head of the encumbent.

It was no hardship for us on twenty below zero nights, clad in woolen pajamas, with our hot water bottles in little flannel bags, made by my grandmother and marked like everything else at Pinewood in chain stitching with the name of the owner, to leap into our snug beds and pull the Turkey red around us.

That sleeping porch is one of my fondest memories of Pinewood: in winter so cozy despite the howling of the wind and the groaning and snapping of the frozen pines and birches outside, the hoot of the Boston and Maine in the distance occasionally interrupting my drowsing; in summer the sweet smells from my grandmother's flower garden below, Lemon Verbena, Marguerite, Sweet William, mingling with the antiseptic fragrance of evergreens and now and then a whiff of salt borne by an easterly breeze from Casco Bay three miles away.

But most of all it was the pines I loved, standing just outside, tall dark queens, protective, embracing, their voices sighing in the wind, their scent exciting, unforgettable. "Pinewood," a trite name for a place perhaps—so many cottages, tourist cabins and hamburg stands on Route 1 from Wychmere to Portland bore the same—but for this place there could be no other name.

That night when we had all three tucked ourselves with our hot water bottles into the red curtained beds on the icy porch, Rachel and I, after Phoebe had gone to sleep, talked about sex.

Rachel had promised me that when she had an opportunity she would explain to me what made babies. Up to this moment, in spite of my considerable knowledge concerning related topics, my information on genetics was vague and peripheral. With considerable zest, Rachel explained the entire procedure from conception to delivery in exceedingly technical terms, reassuring me throughout that it was truly "a beautiful experience." Although I had surmised that the process entailed some kind of union of the male and female, my imagination long since disciplined under Mother's aegis—"Always be pure, girls, even in your thoughts"—had balked at anything so specific. I was thoroughly shocked and repelled by what Rachel told me. When she had finished I lay silent for a long time.

"Mandy?" Rachel's whisper came through the darkness. "Are you asleep?"

"No, I'm just thinking."

"What? What are you thinking?"

I rolled over on my side so she could hear me better.

"I was thinking—you remember at Christmas time—when Mother told us about Aunt Belle killing herself—and all that?"

"Yes."

"Who was the father of her baby? Do you know?" Rachel didn't answer. "You do, *don't* you?"

"Yes, Mandy, I do. Mother told me the next morning. You and Phoebe went skating—and I asked her to tell me—and she did . . ." From my grandmother's bedroom which adjoined the porch came a slight sound, as of a snore. Rachel waited. "We must speak *very* softly—if Vicky hears us talking she'll kill me . . ."

"*Tell* me," I scarcely breathed the words.

"I'll tell you. Mother said I *was* to tell you *and* Phoebe —when you asked me the question. She said we *should* know from *her* when the time came . . ."

"Who was it?" My heart was beating very fast.

"I think you *know* who it was, don't you, Mandy?"

A clammy feeling settled at the back of my neck.

"Yes," I said, "I guess I do."

Neither of us spoke for a moment.

"It explains a lot, doesn't it?" Rachel whispered.

"Yes," I said.

We lay in silence for a long time. Then she spoke again.

"It's late. We must go to sleep now. We can talk tomorrow—but one other thing Mother asked me to tell you—

she forgave them *both*—she especially wanted me to tell you that . . ."

It was several minutes before I could speak.

"I see," I said at last. "Thank you for telling me."

Rachel stretched her arm across the space between our beds and took my hand.

"Mandy, dear, I think you're going to like it here in Wychmere, both you and Phoebe."

"Phoebe will," I said.

"And you will too. A small town is much nicer than the city. You'll know everyone here." She thought for a moment, "You mustn't mind about Father and Mother—and Aunt Belle—any more—they're from a different generation. You have your own life to lead, you know . . ."

"I know."

There was another long pause. I thought she had gone to sleep. Then her whisper came, very faint now—"You know, Mandy, when Mother told me about Aunt Belle's baby I had the strangest feeling—I felt that I'd known it all the time."

"Yes," I said. "I know what you mean. I guess I've known it all the time too."

Presently she was asleep. I could hear her gentle breathing beside me.

The icy branch in the pine tree just outside snapped with a loud report like the crack of a pistol. Then from the distance came the hoot-hoot of the Boston and Maine, an eerie sound in the stillness of the winter night, but for me comforting, nostalgic—a link with the past.

Epilogue

THE RAIN cold and relentless, was still beating against my window. A deep melancholy had settled itself through me, like a drug enervating me. I knew I should get up and go downstairs. I still had things to do about Christmas, Manda's doll's cape to finish, the rocking horse for Thomas to assemble. But my arms and legs felt heavy and I made no effort to move them.

I lay gazing at the photographs on the wall over my desk. How sad the faces looked, as if they were reproaching me for their suffering. Poor Mother, with your wreath of soft hair, your bittersweet smile, I'm glad you don't know about Phoebe and me. Strange that the child brought up largely by my grandmother, "that evil woman," should be the only one to make a success of her marriage, and she the one you feared might be "on the road to destruction" with her six hats.

I had often wondered why it was that Phoebe and I, brought up with so little luxury, so few advantages, compared to Rachel, should be so discontented with our lives, while Rachel had adjusted to hers. Was it that Mother had provided so much for us—not in a material way certainly —but so much understanding, encouragement, tenderness, that no one could ever possibly fill her place?

I looked at the picture of my grandmother, the beautiful Victoria, with her lovelock springing from her tortoise

236

shell comb. Her death had been so horrible, worse in a sense than Mother's, for years a senile old woman confined to her bedroom, useless, incontinent—and then the fire! Her beloved Pinewood had burned to the ground. Rachel, alone there with her, had dragged her by her hair, down the wide staircase, the black bricks searing her arms and legs as they fell. She had died one week later. Nothing was left of Pinewood. Not even the books in the attic were spared, all those handsomely bound volumes. After the fire, when Rachel went over the blackened, water ruined furniture she thought at first glance that the books were intact, but when she picked up one of them it crumbled to ashes in her hand.

My father, crippled with arthritis, was unable to go to Wychmere to his mother's funeral. He had always hated funerals anyway. Now *he* was dead. That last time I saw him, a few weeks before he died, he got up and walked across the room to greet me, but later when he thought I wasn't watching he clung to the wall and shuffling one foot in front of the other returned to his chair. His wife told me too that his new teeth hurt him. I noticed he didn't smile, not once when I was there, though I did my best to make him laugh. In the old days this had been my one claim to his attention, that he thought I was amusing; he had always laughed his boyish laugh whenever I told him an anecdote about some member of the family. Overcome with pity for him that afternoon I spoke to him impulsively:

"I'm sorry, dear, that you feel so poorly."

"I'm all right." He spoke gruffly brushing away my sympathy, as he always had, as his mother always had. "But I'm worried about Phoebe," he added.

"Why?" I asked.

"Why good lord, Amanda, she's down and out most of the time with asthma"—strange to hear Mother's phrase on *his* lips—"Don't you realize what that means? Taking all that cortisone? And her divorce? No money! All those children! What on earth will she *do?*" His voice broke. For a terrible moment I thought he was going to cry.

"You mustn't worry," I said.

"But how can anyone help worrying? Aren't you worried about her?" His eyes, yellow now and hooded, looked at me anxiously as if imploring me to do something before it was too late. I felt he was thinking about what happened to Mother.

"She'll be all *right*," I said. "I know Phoebe and she will. Phoebe's tough—like the rest of us Willards."

But he wasn't listening.

Before I left he took me into what had once been his studio, lined now with pictures of the family: his father and mother, uncles and aunts, his brother, his children and grandchildren, the picture I was looking at now on my wall, of himself when he was at Harvard, in the turtlenecked sweater. This was his hobby now, collecting family photographs.

He had long since given up his painting. There was no trace of any of his oils, of Eva or his other models, but over in one corner of the room under a group of photographs was the oval-framed watercolor of Mother as a girl in the canoe.

"I've always loved that picture," I said, then lightly, "I hope you'll leave it to me in your will."

He made no reply. The expression on his face was stony, impenetrable. But a week after his death a package arrived, carefully wrapped by him weeks before and addressed to me. It was the picture of Mother.

My glance wandered now to the solemn young woman in the bride's dress. Such a trusting, tender, difficult young woman! Why had she rushed headlong into marriage? To have a home? To escape from loneliness? And the young groom standing beside her so smiling, handsome, unsuspecting. What had urged him on?

I thought of my twenty-one-year-old self, just graduated from Radcliffe, in my sister Rachel's apartment in Cambridge. I was to spend ten days there until the start of my summer job in Marblehead as Mother's Helper. Waking up that first morning in the empty apartment (Rachel and Edward had gone to Wychmere to spend the summer with my grandmother) and looking around me at the dusty, fly buzzing bedroom, I realized with a shock that never before had I spent a night alone. Aways surrounded by members of my family, numberless girls at boarding school, camp, college, I had never before that moment known what it meant to be *really* alone. My friends had gone off for the summer, my sisters were gone, my ardent beau of the moment, having urged me in vain to marry him, had gone out West in search of a job. I had had my week at Pinewood. Now I was on my own. I stood it for five days. Then I sent a telegram to Wyoming. A month later I was married.

I glanced from the pictures to my desk piled high with my unfinished manuscripts waiting for me to get back to work after the holidays. Such an activity should be enough to sustain me. But there was still that empty feeling I could never get used to. When my daughters had gone off to college I had thought I would adjust to it, that the ache in my insides would be more bearable as the weeks, months, years went by. I thought of all the hundreds of thousands of women forced to finish their lives alone—"I'll never be a burden to *my* children." How did they do it?

My life stretched ahead of me bleak, meaningless—and the lives of people everywhere around me, so full of suffering, so hopeless. A sensation of sinking back, far far back as if into a deep dark pit came over me, a feeling I had had before and had always managed to pull out of. But now I wondered. Did I *want* to pull out?

I thought again of my mother, so lighthearted and eager

in the beginning, that young girl in the canoe, so full of "gumption" even after her separation from Father, sure she could stand on her "own two feet," make a go of her little household, reduced then to the cramped, pitiful room —a bitter, hopeless woman—and my grandmother in her beautiful house in the pines, lying on her chaise longue gazing out of the window. Was this why she had looked so discontented? Because life had no meaning for her any more?

A trace of annoyance stirred inside me—at myself. Must I remember only the unhappy things about these women? What about Mother's warmth, her gaiety, her courage? My grandmother too had provided something Rachel and Phoebe and I had sorely needed, a framework, a discipline that had helped to make us as "tough" as we were.

The door to my bedroom opened. Manda's dark eyes in her small pale pointed face under the feathery wisps of hair looked at me gravely, asking if she might get up now from her nap—and come in. I held out my arms to her. She ran to my bed, hopped in beside me and snuggled under the quilt, as my sister, Phoebe, had done years before, as my own daughters had done when they were little.

We lay silent for a moment. Then Manda sat up: "Look, Granny! Look!" She pointed at the window.

The long fingers of rain had turned to blobs of mush.

"Oh good!" I said sitting up beside her. "We're going to have a white Christmas after all. Now Santa can come on his sleigh and you and Thomas and I can go coasting tomorrow. Would you like that?"

Manda nodded shyly. Then all at once she put her thin arms around my neck.

"I love you, Granny," she said softly in my ear.

It was enough.